CREATIVE
DO IT YOURSELF

C4C

£ 3.99
WK13

Plumbing and Heating

WARD LOCK

© Ward Lock Limited, 1994
A Cassell Imprint
Villiers House, 41-47 Strand, London WC2N 5JE

Based on *Successful DIY*
© Eaglemoss Publications Limited, 1994

ISBN 0 7063 7278 6

Printed in Spain by Cayfosa Industria Grafica

10 9 8 7 6 5 4 3 2 1

CONTENTS

INTRODUCTION

PLUMBING and central heating make some people nervous because they are largely hidden within the fabric of the house. Often, too, the first sign of a problem is a mess – water dripping through a ceiling, a blocked sink or an overflowing gully or manhole. When something like this happens, you need to know how to minimize the mess by isolating the water supply and fixing the fault as quickly as possible.

This book begins by explaining how the water supply system works and, most importantly, where to look for the stopcocks and gate valves that control the supply of water. A succinct summary of what to do in an emergency is followed by explanations of how to mend burst pipes and leaking connections, repair dripping taps, cure WC and ballvalve malfunctions, and clear blocked traps, waste pipes and drains. Next, the book covers common plumbing jobs such as fitting new taps or plumbing in a washing machine or dishwasher as well as more complex improvements such as fitting an electric shower or a vanity unit.

The book then moves on to heating and insulation, with an invaluable troubleshooting guide to help you track down and cure common problems such as cold central heating radiators and noisy pipes. It also explains how to check the performance of heating controls, and how to clear faults or fit replacements. The book concludes by looking at insulation to reduce unnecessary heat loss and avoid potentially damaging freeze-ups in cold weather.

Clear step-by-step instructions are accompanied by problem solver panels to help if things don't go according to plan and, throughout, compliance with the regulations which govern plumbing work is emphasised. The Building Regulations apply mainly to the safe removal of waste water rather than the supply of clean water, and so have little relevance to the subjects in this book. The Water Supply Byelaws, in contrast, apply to almost all plumbing tasks and the list below includes the most important requirements relating to the jobs in this book. (If you are in any doubt about meeting these requirements when carrying out plumbing work, contact your water supply company for advice.)

- soldered connections on pipes carrying drinking water must be lead-free
- new pipe runs must be easily accessible and must be fitted with isolating taps or valves and drain cocks
- appliances connected to the rising main must be fitted with double check valves to prevent back-siphonage contaminating the water supply
- tap spouts must be at least 20mm ($\frac{1}{8}$in) above the rim of the sink, basin or bath, and there are restrictions on the use of some continental-style mixer taps where hot and cold water are mixed within the tap body.

HOW WATER SYSTEMS WORK

All domestic water is supplied by a *service pipe* connected to the water main in the road. The internal layout varies according to how water is distributed and heated.

The cold water supply

In most homes, cold water used to be supplied **indirectly**. All the cold water outlets except the kitchen sink are fed from a storage tank (*cistern*).

This has several advantages:
- The tank provides an emergency supply if the mains get cut off.
- There is no direct link between appliances and the rising main (apart from the kitchen sink), reducing the chance of contaminated waste water being siphoned back into the mains.
- Water fed from the tank is well below mains pressure, reducing the chance of noisy pipes.

However, there are drawbacks:
- Only the kitchen cold tap should be used for drinking. Cold storage tanks can become contaminated.
- The water pressure in the pipes fed by the storage tank relies on gravity, so the tank must be high enough above the outlets for the water to discharge at a sensible rate. This is not always easy to arrange, particularly in flats.
- The storage tank is usually in the roof, where frost may damage it.

In **direct** systems (increasingly common) all the cold water outlets are supplied directly from the rising main. The main advantages are simpler, cheaper plumbing, the use of every cold tap for drinking, and no problems of insufficient pressure.

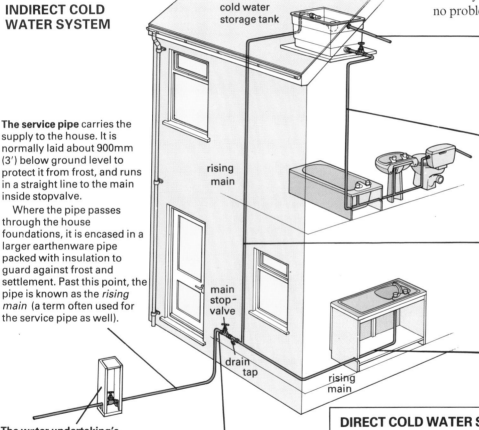

INDIRECT COLD WATER SYSTEM

cold water storage tank

rising main

main stop-valve

drain tap

rising main

The service pipe carries the supply to the house. It is normally laid about 900mm (3') below ground level to protect it from frost, and runs in a straight line to the main inside stopvalve.

Where the pipe passes through the house foundations, it is encased in a larger earthenware pipe packed with insulation to guard against frost and settlement. Past this point, the pipe is known as the *rising main* (a term often used for the service pipe as well).

The water undertaking's stopvalve controlling the mains supply is housed below ground in a clay pipe or brick chamber with a hinged cast-iron or plastic cover plate. Some undertakings have no objection to householders using it, but check first.

The rising main is fitted with a *main stopvalve* (stopcock) shortly after it enters the house (and preferably, though not always, before it branches). There should be a *drain tap*, allowing the rising main to be drained for repairs or alterations.

An overflow pipe from the tank runs to the outside of the house, where it acts as a *warning* that the ballvalve has failed. Most overflows are not capable of diverting a full-scale flood.

Cold feed pipes from the storage tank supply all the other cold water taps, the WC cistern, and – in a vented hot water system – the hot water cylinder.

One branch of the rising main goes to the cold storage tank, and is controlled by a float-operated valve (ballvalve). If 'wet' central heating is installed, a separate branch is taken off this pipe to supply the system's *feed and expansion tank*.

The other branch runs directly to the kitchen sink cold tap. It may have its own stopvalve.

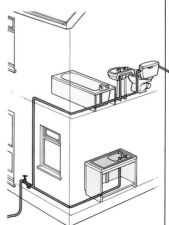

DIRECT COLD WATER SYSTEM

Branches of the rising main supply all the cold taps, the WC cistern, and – in an unvented hot water system – the water heater as well.

7

The hot water supply

This depends on the type of heating installed.

Most houses have what is called a *vented* system, in which water is fed to the heater from a storage tank, and a vent pipe leading back to the tank helps to accommodate expansion of the water as it gets hot. In an indirect cold water system, the cold water storage tank can be used for this. But in a direct cold water system, a vented hot water system has to have its own storage tank, no matter how the other cold outlets are supplied.

In an *unvented* hot water system, the water heater is supplied direct from the rising main and special valves regulate the incoming water pressure. There is no vent pipe. Instead, expansion of the water as it gets hot is accommodated by the heater itself, or by a separate sealed *expansion vessel*; there are also various safety devices to stop the water boiling and guard against pressure build-up.

Each system has its pros and cons. Vented systems need more pipework, plus space for a storage tank, but contain relatively few mechanical components. Unvented systems have more to go wrong, but offer greater design flexibility and in many cases better performance; they don't require a storage tank, so are less vulnerable to frost.

VENTED HOT WATER SYSTEM

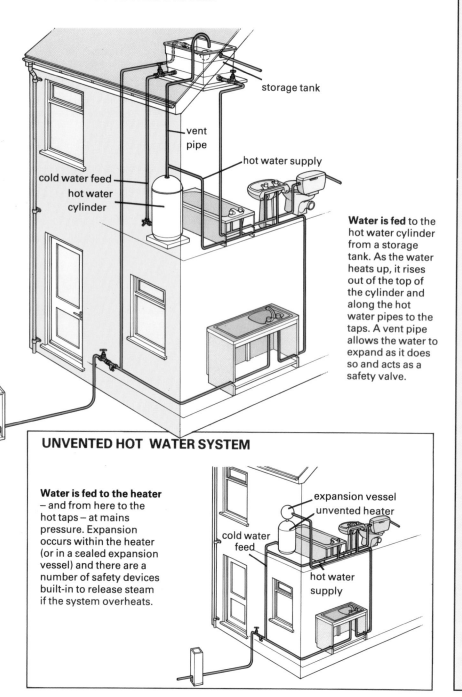

storage tank

vent pipe

hot water supply

cold water feed

hot water cylinder

Water is fed to the hot water cylinder from a storage tank. As the water heats up, it rises out of the top of the cylinder and along the hot water pipes to the taps. A vent pipe allows the water to expand as it does so and acts as a safety valve.

UNVENTED HOT WATER SYSTEM

Water is fed to the heater – and from here to the hot taps – at mains pressure. Expansion occurs within the heater (or in a sealed expansion vessel) and there are a number of safety devices built-in to release steam if the system overheats.

expansion vessel
unvented heater

cold water feed

hot water supply

DIFFERENT TYPES OF WATER HEATER

If your hot water system is vented, you may have:

An electric immersion heater, which heats the water inside a hot water cylinder. Sometimes two are fitted.

A water heating boiler, which heats the water and transfers it to a hot water cylinder. There may be a back-up immersion heater.

Central heating, in which water heated by the boiler heats the water inside the hot water cylinder via a coiled *heat exchanger*. Again, there may be a back-up immersion heater.

If your hot water system is unvented, you may have:

A separate 'instantaneous' gas or electric heater. Single-point heaters supply one hot tap while multi-point heaters supply several taps. Larger versions also have a built-in hot water storage tank.

A combination system (eg 'Combi') in which a central heating boiler and 'instantaneous' heater are combined with a small storage tank.

WHAT TO DO IN AN EMERGENCY

The floods caused by leaking or burst pipes can result in damage on a grand scale, bringing down ceilings and ruining decorations and furnishings.

In temperate climates, the combination of unexpected frost and inadequate insulation is still the major culprit. But faulty pipework, worn fittings and DIY accidents all account for their fair share of emergencies, so wherever you live it pays to know what to do when disaster strikes – and to be prepared at all times.

■ Make sure you know where your stopcocks are and which pipes they control. Ensure they all work.

■ Keep emergency repair materials (see Shopping List) in the house.

The following repairs are designed to get you by until the damage can be repaired more permanently.

.... Shopping List ....

Shopping is the last thing you want to do when faced with a flood, so be prepared.

Two-part epoxy putty (A) will plug almost any kind of leak and is useful for countless other repair jobs around the home. *Car body filler* is an effective substitute, but less easy to handle.

Two-part adhesive tape (B) is another handy repair material, especially for sealing burst soldered joints in copper pipes.

PTFE tape (C) makes it possible to re-make burst compression joints.

Potatoes (D) have saved many a plumber – if a pipe comes adrift, shove a potato over the end.

Repair kits for pipes (E) are inexpensive, and worth buying.

EMERGENCY CHECKLIST

PIPE ALREADY BURST

Don't panic!
If you are alone...
Turn off the water supply
☐ Do this as close to the leaking pipe as possible. If you can't find a stopcock, or it is jammed, turn off at the main stopcock. Failing this, if you have a cold storage tank and central heating expansion tank, tie up their ballvalves to stop water entering.
☐ Switch off the central heating, immersion heater, or any other water heating appliances. (If the flood is near electrical outlets, switch off at the main switch by the consumer unit or fusebox).
☐ Open all the taps to relieve pressure on the leak and get rid of any water left in the system.

If there are others in the house, get someone else to carry out the above steps while you...
☐ Locate the exact source of the leak.
☐ If the pipe has failed at a joint and it will pull apart, shove a potato on the end to stem the flow. (If the water is at mains pressure, bend the pipe or wedge something against the potato to hold it in place.)
☐ Otherwise, tie a cloth around the leak to contain it while you decide what to do next.

YOU BURST PIPE

☐ If you did it with a nail or screw, leave this where it is (it will at least contain the flow) while you turn off the water as described above.
☐ If you did it with a drill, drive a screw part-way into the hole to stem the flow. Then turn off the water and heating.

WATER POURING FROM OVERFLOW

☐ Locate which tank or cistern the pipe is connected to and tie up the affected ballvalve (the cause of the trouble). Turn off the supply to the tank.

WATER BOILING IN PIPES

☐ Turn off water heating.
☐ Leave system to cool down.
☐ Open hot taps to check water supply to hot water cylinder, which if the heating has been off during a frost may be blocked by an ice plug.
☐ If supply is OK, call plumber to replace faulty central heating or cylinder thermostat.

For lead pipes see Problem Solver, page 12

AVOIDING DISASTERS

Efficiently heated, properly insulated homes are well protected against bursts caused by freezing. Even so, it's worth checking for vulnerable areas before the start of each cold season.

■ Make sure all pipes and storage tanks are insulated. But don't insulate underneath tanks in a roof space – heat rising from below helps to protect them.

■ Check that the existing insulation hasn't been disturbed or displaced. Watch out for lids left off storage tanks, or insulating jackets which have been allowed to slip down.

Pipe bends and the areas around stopcocks also have a habit of 'losing' their insulation – refix it with lengths of twisted wire.

■ Leave the heating on low if you leave the house during winter. For an extended absence, it's as well to turn off the water and drain down the entire system (but not the central heating).

■ Even in centrally heated homes, pipes against outside walls or in extensions and outhouses are particularly vulnerable to frost. Make sure these areas are kept warm.

■ Check where the rising main enters the house. This area is often overlooked when insulating.

■ Don't forget to turn off the supply to an outside tap before the cold weather starts.

And the rest of the year . . .

■ Beware of drilling or fixing into walls and floors where pipes may run. Look first, or check with a metal detector.

■ Watch out for pipes around radiators, which are especially prone to accidental knocks.

■ Treat lead pipes and their stopcocks with extra respect. Most lead pipework is at an age where the slightest movement may cause it to disintegrate.

■ Check that your bathroom fittings and tanks all have overflow pipes connected to the drains or to outside. The previous occupants may have 'forgotten' to fit one, probably because it was inconvenient to arrange (though this is against the Building Regulations).

Frozen pipes

If you suspect your pipes have frozen, try all the taps until you've located the approximate location of the freeze-up. If the trouble is on the rising main, storage tank or cold feed pipe to the hot water cylinder, turn off the heating as a precaution.

You can thaw the ice plug using one of the methods shown. But first, be prepared for a leak when the ice melts.

Check your house (below) for areas vulnerable to frost before every cold season. The rest of the year, watch out for blocked or missing overflows, and pipes that are prone to accidental damage.

flood danger: overflow blocked or missing

vulnerable to frost: exposed rising main

vulnerable to frost: pipes in poorly heated area

vulnerable to frost: outdoor tap

THAWING FROZEN PIPES

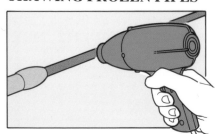

Hot air: *If possible, play a hair dryer over the suspect area. Warm the whole pipe, so that the ice plug disperses quickly as soon as it begins to melt.*

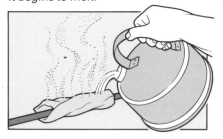

Boiling water: *Alternatively, wrap cloth over the pipe and pour on boiling water. Don't apply the water direct, or you risk doing more damage.*

vulnerable to frost:
slipped insulating
jacket/lid left off tank

vulnerable to frost:
slipped pipe insulation

prone to accidental damage:
radiator pipes and joints

prone to accidental damage:
pipes under floors and in walls

MENDING A BURST

How you make a temporary repair
depends on where the burst is.

■ If it's in the middle of a pipe and
there's space, use a clamp-type
repair kit or improvise your own
(see overleaf).

■ If it's at a compression joint,
undo the cover nut and wrap PTFE
tape around the sealing ring, then
retighten.

■ If it's at a soldered joint, cover
the joint with layers of two-part
repair tape or a sleeve of epoxy
putty (see overleaf).

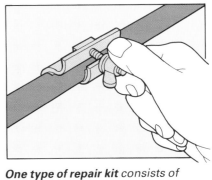

One type of repair kit consists of
two clamping plates. Lay the one
with the rubber seal over the
burst, interlock the other, then
tighten the wing nut to hold them.

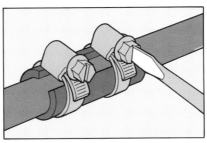

Another kit uses Jubilee clips.
Lay the seal over the burst and
position the metal clamping
plates. Undo the clips, fit them
over the plates, and tighten.

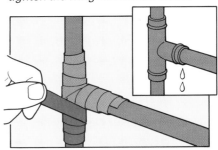

Bind a burst soldered joint with
two-part repair tape. Wind on a
layer of one tape, cover with a
layer of the second, then finish
with another of the first.

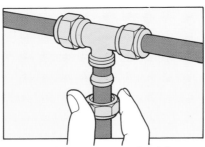

1 *For a burst compression joint,*
begin by loosening off the
cover nut with an adjustable
spanner. Slide back the nut to
reveal the sealing ring (olive).

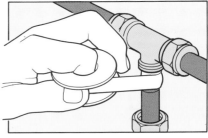

2 Wind a few turns of PTFE tape
around the sealing ring, plus
a little more around the threaded
joint connector. Replace the cover
nut and tighten.

STORAGE TANK EMERGENCIES

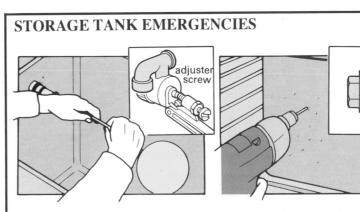

adjuster
screw

If the overflow is running, the
ballvalve is at fault. Try bending
the float arm down to exert more
closing pressure (on a plastic
valve screw in the adjuster).
Otherwise, tie up the float arm.

To plug a pin-hole leak in an old
metal tank, first tie up the
ballvalve and drain it. Drill out the
hole and fit a nut and bolt with a
washer both sides. Replace tank
as soon as possible.

ACCIDENTAL DAMAGE

If possible, leave whatever caused the damage in the pipe while you turn off the water and drain down the pipe.

Where the pipe is bedded in a solid wall, you won't have space to use a repair kit – use epoxy putty or car body filler instead. This makes a substantial repair that will last for some time if left undisturbed. However, it's as well to make a proper repair before making good the damage to the surrounding plaster or you could have problems later.

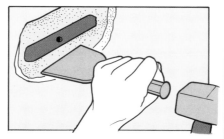

1 Use a builder's bolster or an old wood chisel to hack away the plaster around the area of the burst. Take care not to cause any more damage to the pipe.

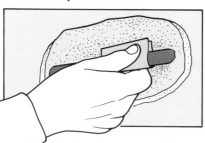

2 Rub the damaged part of the pipe with sandpaper until it becomes shiny. Then clean the whole area with white spirit or methylated spirit (alcohol).

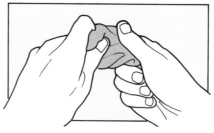

3 For epoxy putty, knead together pieces from both packs. (For car filler, mix up the resin with a little of the hardener on a piece of wood.)

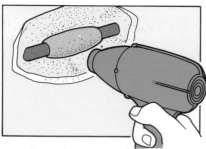

4 Press the repair mixture over and around the hole (but not too hard, or you'll block the pipe). Then play a hair dryer over it to speed hardening.

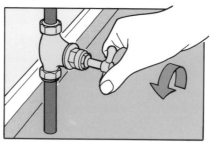

5 When the repair feels hard, you can restore a low-pressure supply – open the stopcock just a little. After a day, restore the supply to normal.

Trade tip

Your own repair kit

‘ If you're caught unprepared, wrap anything you can around the burst – belt, floorcloth, or some such – and make up your own repair kit as follows:

Take a piece of ordinary garden hose about 100mm (4") long and slice it down the middle. Lay the two halves opposite each other over the burst – then secure with pieces of thin coathanger wire every 12mm (½") or so. Twist the wire ends tightly using pliers. ’

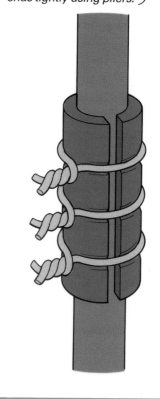

■ PROBLEM SOLVER ■

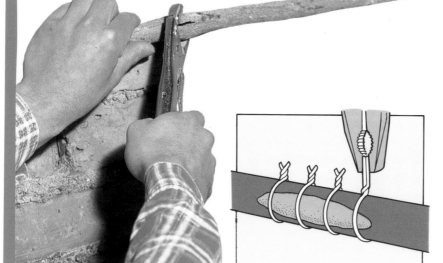

Dealing with lead pipes

When a lead pipe bursts it usually splits, so try the following repair:
■ Pinch the split closed with a self-grip wrench – set the jaws wide open, so they bear on the split area, not the whole pipe.
■ Fill what remains of the split with epoxy putty or car body filler as described above.
■ Wrap stiff wire – 30A fuse wire or thin coathanger wire – tightly around the pipe to support the repair and hold the filler in place.

If a lead pipe disintegrates completely, saw through it with a hacksaw, hammer the end closed, and fill with putty.

Support the epoxy putty repair with twists of stiff wire.

WHERE TO TURN THE WATER OFF

Before you can do any plumbing job, whether it's changing a tap washer or mending a leak, you need to know where to turn the water off. These pages cover everything you need to know about turning off the hot and cold supplies – but not central heating, which is covered on pages 65-72.

All household plumbing systems contain stopcocks or gate valves for isolating the water supply. The basic procedure is:
■ Turn off the heating as a safety precaution.
■ Find the nearest stopcock to the pipe or outlet you want to isolate (this will vary from job to job).
■ Turn the stopcock **clockwise** as far as it will go.
■ Open the tap at the end of the pipe run to drain any water left in the pipework (this may take a few seconds).

Unfortunately, there are no 'rules' about where stopcocks might be placed: some houses have more than others, and only rarely is there one for every section of pipe. So before you try to find out which stopcock controls which pipes, have a look at the diagram on the right, which shows how water flows around the house.

Cold supply This enters the house under mains pressure. In many systems the pipe then splits into two, one branch serving the kitchen sink cold tap and the other the cold storage tank in the roof. In some systems, however, there is no storage tank; the pipe simply divides into branches serving the different outlets so all the cold water is at mains pressure. The diagram shows a storage tank system, but all systems work on the same principle.

From the cold storage tank, further pipes serve the remaining cold outlets and the hot water cylinder. The water in these pipes is not under mains pressure: it relies on gravity, which means that the higher the tank, the greater the 'push' the water gets.

Hot supply The pressure of the water in the hot pipes is governed by the pressure of the cold water. This is because as the water gets heated in the cylinder or water heater, it rises above the cold water being fed in below it; the pressure of the cold water then literally forces the hot water out into the pipes. In other words, stop the cold water and the hot water stops too – a useful point to remember when there isn't a stopcock where you'd expect to find one.

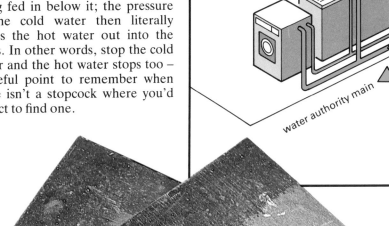

KEY
Cold water under high (mains) pressure
Cold under low pressure
Hot water

water authority main

Trade tip

Now's the time to try

❝ I always tell people to find out where their stopcocks are as soon as they move into a house – far better to do it when you've got the time, than when there's an emergency and you've got a flood to deal with.

As you find each one, turn it off and test which pipes it serves by opening all the likely taps or checking the ballvalves in the cold storage tank and WC cistern.

It's a good idea to label the stopcocks with their function, ie 'bathroom cold water', so that anyone else in the house can find them in a hurry if they need to. ❞

KITCHEN COLD WATER 4½ TURNS FROM OFF

WHERE TO LOOK FOR YOUR STOPCOCKS

BATHROOM APPLIANCES

1

ALL HOT WATER

2

cold water supply

hot water cylinder (or heater)

ALL HOT WATER AND ALL COLD WATER NOT MAINS-FED

3

cold water supply

cold water feeds

vent pipe

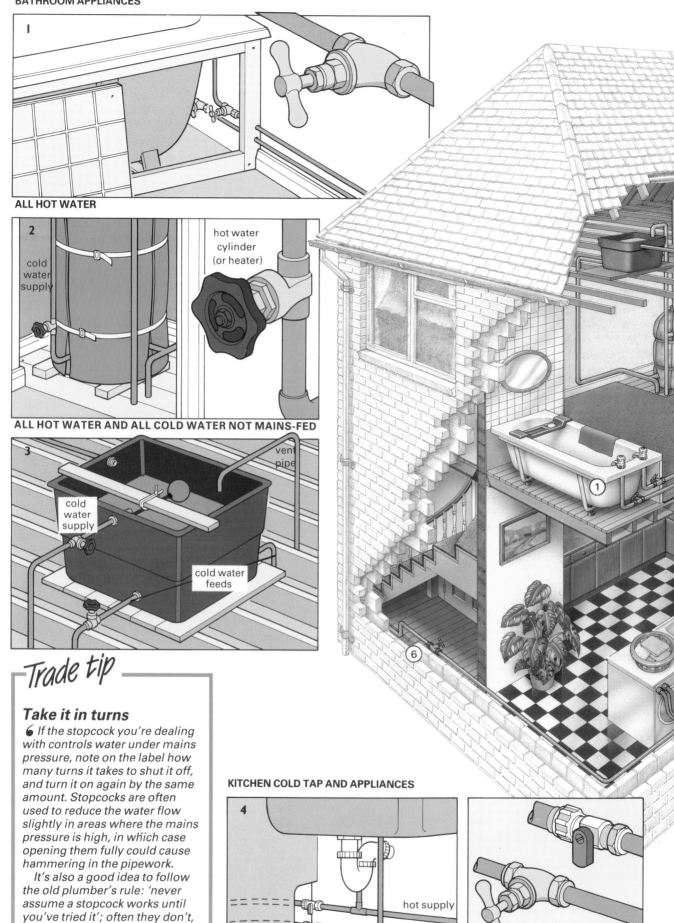

① ⑥

Trade tip

Take it in turns

❛ If the stopcock you're dealing with controls water under mains pressure, note on the label how many turns it takes to shut it off, and turn it on again by the same amount. Stopcocks are often used to reduce the water flow slightly in areas where the mains pressure is high, in which case opening them fully could cause hammering in the pipework.

It's also a good idea to follow the old plumber's rule: 'never assume a stopcock works until you've tried it'; often they don't, and you need to try another one further down the line. ❜

KITCHEN COLD TAP AND APPLIANCES

4

hot supply

branch from rising main

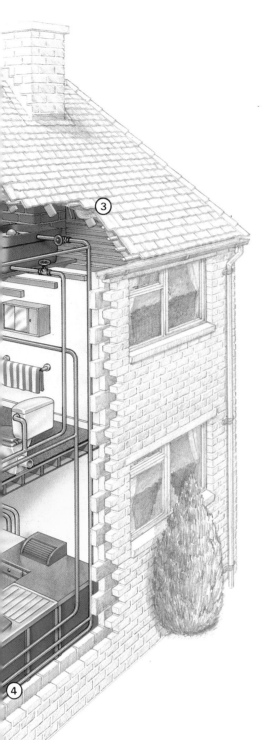

As a general rule, start at the easiest place and work back towards the main stopcock.

Bathroom appliances

1 Bathroom appliances sometimes have stopcocks for each supply pipe, or one set that shuts off all the bathroom water. Be prepared for them to be hidden behind the bath panel or any boxing-in that's been used to conceal the pipes.

All hot water

2 If you can't find any local stopcocks, the ideal place to turn off all the hot water is at the cold feed to the hot water cylinder or heater. Look for a stopcock near the base, and check that the pipe it's on feels cold.

All hot water and all cold water not mains fed

3 Often, stopcocks are fitted to the feed pipes from the storage tank to the hot cylinder and bathroom cold taps.

Failing this, you can isolate all

pipes that aren't on the rising main by shutting off the supply to the tank and then draining it down by turning on all the cold taps. This will take some time, and can leave the system prone to airlocks, so only try it as a last resort.

If there is no stopcock on the supply pipe (the one feeding the ballvalve in the tank), tie up the ballvalve itself as shown.

Kitchen cold tap and appliances

4 There may be a stopcock somewhere in the kitchen to shut off the branch of the rising main that feeds the sink cold tap. Other kitchen appliances, such as a washing machine or dish washer, should have shut-off valves on both supply pipes. The same goes for other ground-floor appliances fed direct from the rising main, and also for outdoor taps.

All water

5 The rising main stopcock shuts off all the water, and it's rare for houses not to have one (though not impossible). Look for it where the main enters the house: under the stairs or behind the kitchen sink are the most common locations. In flats and maisonettes it will be on the first branch off the main supply to the rest of the building, probably near the sink or the water heater.

6 Sometimes, however, the main stopcock is found under the floorboards – often near the front door, or, if the kitchen has been extended, where the old sink was.

Search for a small section of floorboard that looks as if it has been cut and lifted in the past. Lever it up with a bolster chisel (at a pinch, use a garden spade).

7 Most houses also have a water authority stopcock which isolates the entire water supply before it enters the building, so if all else fails you can try this. You'll find it under an iron cover on the pavement, or in the garden near the road. The stopcock itself will be about 1m (3ft) below the ground, and may be covered by layers of mud; dig this out by hand with a piece of coat hanger wire.

To turn the stopcock, you need a special key (available from plumber's merchants) or a strong piece of wood with a V shaped notch cut in the end. Alternatively, the engineer's department of your local water authority will do it for you, but give them a day's notice.

ALL WATER

iron cover

rising main

ALL WATER

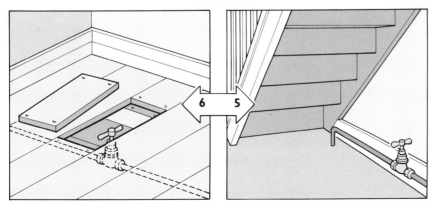

When it won't budge

When stopcocks haven't been used for a while they have a nasty habit of refusing to move (gate valves, which work slightly differently, are more reliable).

In this case, the first thing to do is squirt some penetrating oil around the spindle mechanism and leave it for half an hour before trying again.

If this doesn't work, wrap the stopcock in an old floorcloth and pour on boiling water; the heat may release it.

Your only other options are to apply more heat – from a blow torch or electric paint stripper – or more force. But before you use force a word of warning: if the pipes either side of the stopcock are lead, the chances are they will crack. If possible, find another stopcock further down the line rather than risk a burst.

To get extra leverage, slip a piece of pipe over one side of the handle. Alternatively, use an adjustable wrench with some cloth between the jaws to stop the handle getting chewed up. Relieve the strain on the pipework by supporting it with a piece of wood.

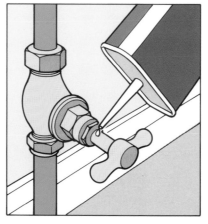

Try freeing a seized stopcock with penetrating oil . . .

. . . or wrap it in an old cloth and pour on boiling water.

Minor leaks

After freeing a stopcock you might find that it leaks slightly from around the spindle area. To cure this, loosen the top (gland) nut on the spindle and wind a few turns of plumber's jointing tape (PTFE tape – available from any hardware store) round the threaded spindle body. Then retighten the nut a little over hand-tight – any more, and you won't be able to turn the handle.

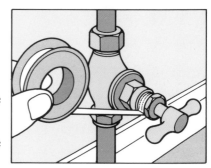

Use PTFE tape to seal a leaking stopcock spindle.

Airlocks

Sometimes, when you turn the water back on, you hear a hissing and gurgling in the pipes and no water comes out of the taps. Usually, the pipes affected are those fed from the storage tank, where the pressure is low.

Depending on where the problem is, you may be able to force the airlock back up the pipe by taking a damp cloth and plunging vigorously against the spout of the affected tap; when the air reaches the tank it will be able to escape.

If this doesn't work, connect a hose between the affected tap and one that's supplied at mains pressure (securing the ends with Jubilee clips).

Turn both taps on and leave them for about 30 seconds, then turn the mains tap off and check to see if the airlock has cleared. Sometimes it takes several goes, so be patient.

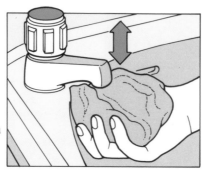

Try pumping an airlocked tap with a damp rag to create suction and force the airlock down the pipe.

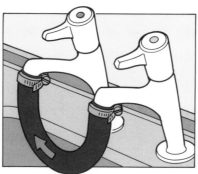

If this doesn't work, see if you can force out the airlock by connecting to a mains-fed tap.

—Trade tip—

Avoiding airlocks

❝ Airlocks can take ages to clear, so wherever possible I try to avoid them. If I've had to drain the cold storage tank, for example, I'll let the water back in as slowly as possible so that the air in the pipes has a chance to escape as they fill up.

If you then get persistent airlocks, the trouble may be that the storage tank isn't filling up as quickly as it is being drained, so the pipes are sucking in air instead of water. You can check this by watching the tank while someone is filling the bath to see whether the tank empties before the bath is full. If so, the trouble may be that the stopcock hasn't been turned back on fully or that you have a faulty ball-valve controlling the supply to the tank. ❞

MENDING LEAKS IN PIPEWORK

Where a pipe or joint has already burst, calling for emergency repairs, there remains the problem of how to repair the damage permanently. Fortunately, modern plumbing fittings have put the job firmly within the scope of the do-it-yourselfer – even when the damage is on an old iron or lead pipe.

All of the repairs shown here use basic plumbing tools – wrenches for undoing pipes, hacksaws for cutting them, and PTFE tape for remaking the joints. In the case of soldered joints, you'll also need a blowtorch and heat-proof mat, plus supplies of self-cleaning flux and solder. When it comes to buying new pipe and fittings, the important thing is to know what pipe size you're dealing with. If necessary, check the external diameter and quote this to your supplier.

LEAKING COMPRESSION JOINTS

Most leaks on compression joints are caused by over or undertightening; the difficulty is knowing which.

If there is some thread left showing, try tightening the nut (clockwise) a half-turn. If this doesn't work – or there is no visible thread to start with – turn off the water, drain down the pipe, and dismantle the leaking side of the fitting.

Check that the pipe end reaches as far as the internal stop, with the sealing ring (olive) hard against the fitting. If the pipe is too short, you'll have to patch in a new section (see overleaf). If the olive is wrongly positioned, you *may* be able to tap it further along the pipe. However, it's safer to saw through the old

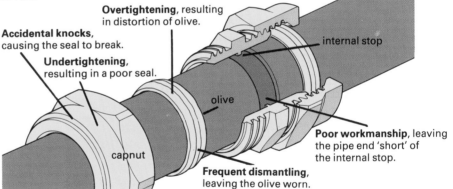

Overtightening, resulting in distortion of olive.

Accidental knocks, causing the seal to break.

Undertightening, resulting in a poor seal.

internal stop

olive

capnut

Poor workmanship, leaving the pipe end 'short' of the internal stop.

Frequent dismantling, leaving the olive worn.

olive with a hacksaw – taking care not to damage the pipe end – then fit a new one.

If everything looks OK, wrap a couple of turns of PTFE tape around the fitting side of the olive, keeping it clear of the cut pipe end, or lightly smear it with jointing compound (eg Boss Blue, Fernox XLS). Then remake the joint.

LEAKING THREADED JOINTS

Old-fashioned threaded joints in iron pipe were sealed with hemp and linseed oil compound. After years in service, the hemp can rot and allow water to seep through – although this usually results in an annoying drip rather than a jet of water.

The problem is easily remedied providing you can unscrew the pipe. But this means starting at a free end or a union, so you may have to dismantle several good joints to get at the faulty one.

1 Undo the necessary joints, using a Stillson-type wrench to grip the threaded pipe. If any are stiff, apply a little heat to soften the old jointing compound.

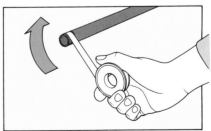

2 Scrape off all traces of old compound from the thread, and wrap it with at least five clockwise turns of PTFE tape before remaking each joint.

LEAKING SOLDERED JOINTS

Leaks in soldered joints are usually caused by dirt stopping the solder running freely in the first place. So long as the pipe can be drained **completely** it's usually possible to solve the problem by heating the joint with a blowtorch, and then feeding in a generous amount of self-cleaning flux followed immediately by a short length of solder. This works on pre-soldered joints as well as the end feed type.

Otherwise, it's best to fit a new joint. Sever the old one in the middle, then heat up both sides and remove them. Clean and resolder.

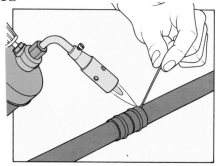

Patch an existing joint by heating until the solder bubbles, then feeding in fresh flux and solder. If the solder is drawn in, you know it has worked.

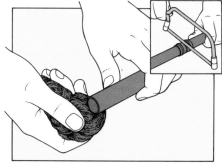

To dismantle a leaking joint, saw through the middle (inset), then heat both sides to remove the cut fitting. Clean off all traces of old solder with steel wool.

REPAIRING COPPER PIPE

Burst or damaged sections of copper pipe are best cut out and replaced with new (but see Tip opposite). A frost damaged pipe is likely to have expanded well beyond the actual burst, making it difficult to fit new joints, so don't be tempted to skimp on materials – cut out at least 300mm (12″).

Where the pipe is rigidly fixed between two points it may be difficult to insert a new section with conventional couplings. There are two ways to overcome this problem.
■ Use special *slip couplings*. These have no internal stops, allowing them to be slipped on to the old pipe ends and then slid back again over the joint once the new section is in position. Slip couplings are available in both compression and pre-soldered form.
■ Fit a *flexible connector*, which can be bent by hand to fit the gap. Flexible connectors are available with compression, soldered or push-fit joints, and come in various lengths. You shouldn't need to fit new pipe as well, but make sure you have the connector with you before cutting out the damaged section, and don't forget to allow some overlap.

On balance, flexible connectors are more convenient than slip couplings but may not look as neat.

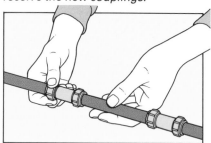

1 *Cut out the damaged section of pipe with a junior hacksaw. File off any burrs and clean the pipe ends thoroughly, ready to receive the new couplings.*

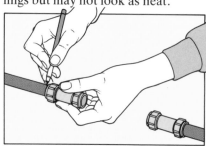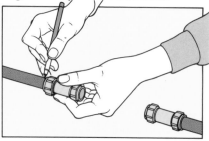

2 *If using slip couplings, slide them over the pipe ends and mark their final positions in pencil. This helps when it comes to placing them over the joints.*

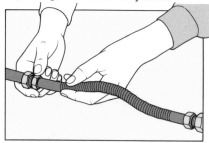

3 *Mark and cut the new section to fit the gap exactly. Prepare the ends and offer it up, then slide the couplings over it and make the joints.*

Bend a flexible connector to fit the gap and make the joints. The corrugated type can't withstand repeated bending, so take care to get it right first time.

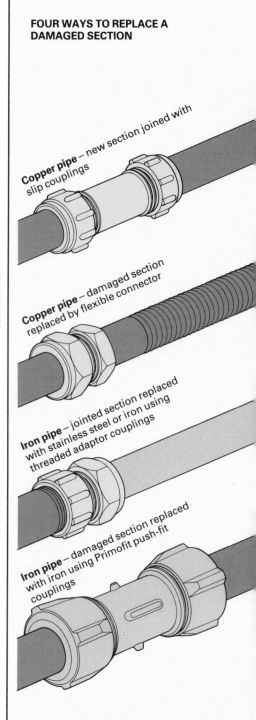

FOUR WAYS TO REPLACE A DAMAGED SECTION

Copper pipe – new section joined with slip couplings

Copper pipe – damaged section replaced by flexible connector

Iron pipe – jointed section replaced with stainless steel or iron using threaded adaptor couplings

Iron pipe – damaged section replaced with iron using Primofit push-fit couplings

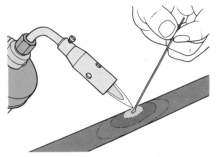

Fill a small hole with a blob of solder. Polish the pipe with steel wool first, smear on some flux, then gently melt the solder over the hole.

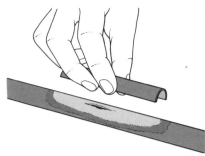

For a larger hole, heat the fluxed pipe and melt on solder to cover the damaged area. Then position the fluxed patch, heat again, and feed in more solder.

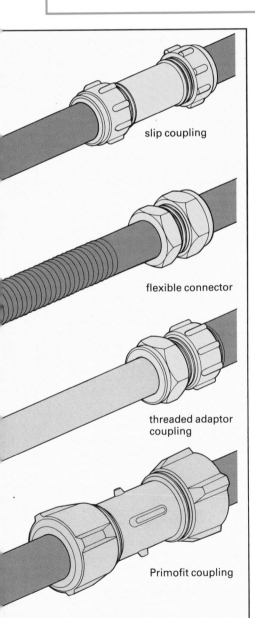

slip coupling

flexible connector

threaded adaptor coupling

Primofit coupling

REPAIRING IRON PIPE

There are three ways to repair iron pipe, depending on the extent of the damaged area, and on what materials you can get hold of.

If the damaged area is small and there is at least 25mm (1″) clearance around the pipe, buy a single *Johnston coupling* and use this to seal the hole.

Where the damage extends over a larger area, you have two choices:
■ Cut out the old section of pipe and fit a new piece of iron pipe between two Johnston couplings or *Primofit* push-fit joints.
■ Unscrew the complete damaged section at the nearest threaded joints, and fit a new section using *adaptor couplings*. This may be easier where space around the pipe is limited, though you could have to remove several sections to get at the damaged one.

In this case, use plastic or stainless steel for the replacement section (but not copper, which sets up an electro-chemical reaction with iron that eventually causes the pipework to corrode). Choose the nearest matching diameter – eg 15mm plastic for ½″ iron – then buy couplings to suit. There are versions for both stainless steel and plastic, with threaded joints on one side and compression joints on the other.

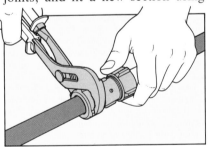

For a small hole, saw through the pipe, ease open the cut and insert a Johnston coupling. Slide it over the cut and tighten the nuts with an adjustable wrench.

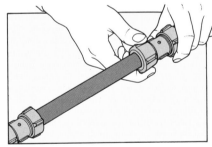

For more extensive damage, cut out a section of pipe and fit a new piece. Use Johnston couplings or Primofit joints to avoid having to make threaded joints.

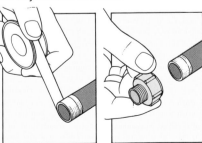

To replace a complete section, dismantle the run back to the nearest threaded joint. Clean the thread, wrap on PTFE tape, and fit a threaded adaptor . . .

. . . then cut a new section of plastic or stainless steel pipe and compression-joint it to the adaptor. Repeat at the other end, then reassemble the run.

JOINING TO LEAD·PIPE

Modern joint fittings like those on the right have made it possible to repair lead pipe without having to worry about traditional 'wiped joints'. After cutting out the damaged section, simply join in a new section of copper pipe of the equivalent internal diameter.

The only difficult part is measuring the old pipe so that you know what size fitting to buy. Lead pipe varies in wall thickness according to its grade, so look for identification marks stamped on it giving the weight and bore size – eg 'BS 602 ¾"×11lbs'.

If you can't find any stamp (very old pipe may not have one), either take the old damaged section with you to the merchants, or cut the pipe and then measure both the bore and the wall thickness.

When cutting out the old section, take care to support the pipe so that you don't cause any damage further along the run. Remove any burrs with a file or metal rasp, then cut the new copper section to the exact size of the gap.

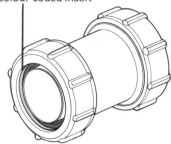

colour-coded insert

'Philmac' plastic couplings have colour-coded inserts for various pipe materials and sizes.

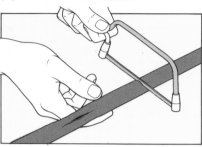

1 Saw the lead pipe with a hacksaw or coarse toothed 'Universal' saw. Cut far enough past the damage to leave you with the true size of the pipe.

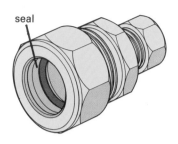

seal

'Leadlock' fittings come in different sizes and types – eg lead-lead, lead-copper.

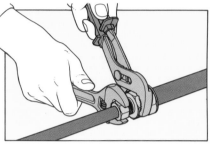

2 Join in the new section of copper pipe using a pair of your chosen fittings. Take care to assemble them in the right order then tighten the nuts.

■ PROBLEM SOLVER ■

When you can't turn the water off . . .

If you can't turn the water off – either because of a faulty stopcock, or because there isn't one – use a pipe freezer to stem the flow temporarily.

Professional pipe freezers can be hired, but it's usually easier to buy a freezing kit (eg 'Artic') consisting of an aerosol spray and freezing muff which you tie over the pipe. These kits are perfectly capable of coping with mains pressure pipes – which is usually where they are most needed.

Using a pipe freezer
Plan things thoroughly before you start: have all your tools to hand, plus a suitable size flexible connector, or a new section of pipe and slip couplings. You also need a watch or timer to time the cooling process, which is critical to the successful formation of an ice plug that will completely block the flow of water.

Aim to complete the job as quickly as possible, but don't panic – the ice plug will remain in place for up to half an hour.

Leaks in plastic pipe
The problem with repairing plastic supply pipes is knowing what type of plastic they are. **cPVC** pipe (generally white) has solvent-welded joints. Simply cut back to the nearest joints, then join in a new piece.
Polyethylene-based pipe (blue or black) can be push-fit or compression jointed (using steel reinforcing sleeves). However, its often easier to buy a copper flexible connector and use this to replace the damaged section.

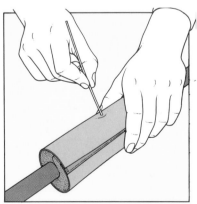

1 *Select an area to freeze,* at least 600mm (2') **upstream** of the damaged part. Fit the tube to the muff and secure the ends tightly around the pipe.

2 Fit the can to the tube and spray in the freezing agent. Wait the recommended amount of time for the ice plug to form, then get to work.

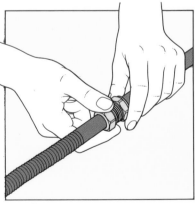

3 Cut out the damaged section and fit a flexible connector or a new piece of pipe and slip couplings. Then simply wait for the ice plug to melt.

REPAIRING LEAKING TAPS

Taps are usually the hardest working components in a plumbing system, so it's hardly surprising if they develop the occasional fault.

Leaking from the spout is usually due to a worn or split washer – the part that seals the tap's inlet. So long as you know where to turn off the water, fitting a new washer is a simple job requiring only basic tools. And if this doesn't cure the problem, it's usually possible to regrind the seat – the part the washer closes against. This is much easier (and cheaper) than replacing the tap – see page 24.

Leaking from the handle, or a handle that's hard to turn, are two faults to do with the tap mechanism. Since you'll be exposing this to replace the washer, it's worth servicing it as well – see page 23.

Spare parts for taps are sold by plumber's merchants and hardware stores First identify what type and size of tap you're dealing with (see below). Then, if possible, take the old parts with you so that you can buy matching replacements. Failing this, make sure you can describe the tap and what it is fitted to.

Washers, seals and other parts are cheap, so buy a set of spares so that you don't get caught out again. Also, buy a tube of silicone gel for lubricating the mechanism.

KNOW YOUR TAPS

Taps come in many styles (see below), but work in one of two ways:

Washered taps (left) have a spindle mechanism, on the end of which is a backing plate (jumper) holding the washer. Turning the handle closes the washer against the inlet (seat), shutting off the water.

Washers need replacing at intervals, as do the seals around the spindle. It's also possible for the seat to wear or become damaged.

Ceramic disc taps (right) have a pair of finely ground discs which open and close the water inlet as the handle (often a simple lever) is moved through a quarter turn.

The diamond-hard discs are supposedly maintenance-free, but faults have been known to occur and most manufacturers offer free replacement cartridges for taps under five years old. The cartridges come in left (hot) and right (cold) versions and aren't interchangeable.

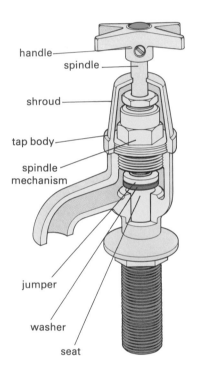

- handle
- spindle
- shroud
- tap body
- spindle mechanism
- jumper
- washer
- seat

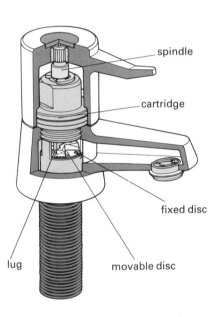

- spindle
- cartridge
- fixed disc
- lug
- movable disc

Pillar taps come in two inlet sizes – ½" for sink and basin taps, ¾" for baths.

Older styles have chromed brass capstan handles and shrouds; newer designs have clear acrylic handles. Ceramic disc versions often have levers.

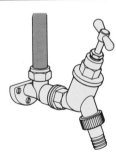

Bib taps are for outside use and utility rooms, and are normally the ½" size. They work in the same way as washered pillar taps and take the same washers, but use leather washers outside for increased frost resistance.

Supataps can be rewashered without turning off the water. The special washers come ready-fitted to a brass backing plate (jumper), but vary widely between models and aren't easy to find; if you do, buy plenty of spares.

Mixer taps for the kitchen may be *two-hole* or *monobloc* (single hole), with washered or ceramic disc mechanisms.

A swivel spout may leak around its base when the seals inside wear out, but these are easily replaced.

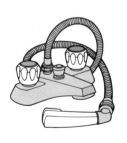

Bath shower mixers, like sink mixers, may have washered or disc mechanisms.

Water is switched from spout to shower head by a washered *diverter mechanism.* When water comes out of both outlets, washer needs renewing.

CHANGING WASHERS

Start the job by turning off the water and opening the tap to drain down what's left in the pipe.

Next, gain access to the tap mechanism. On plastic handled taps, the handle pulls off, or is held by a screw under the coloured insert (prise this up with a screwdriver).

On brass taps, unscrewing the shroud will often leave enough room to get a spanner on the mechanism nut. If not, undo the handle – held by a small grub screw – and remove the shroud completely. (See Problem Solver for problem handles.)

Washer fittings vary widely (see Step 2), so have a small crosshead screwdriver and a pair of long nosed pliers handy. If you can't get the old washer off, or the new one is a loose fit, prise off the jumper and fit a new combined washer/jumper or a plastic insert (see overleaf).

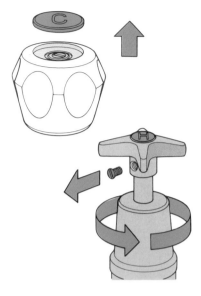

Plastic handles have a hidden screw or pull off the spindle. *Brass handles* are held by a small screw. The shroud unscrews.

Trade tip
Washer wise

❝ If you're stuck without a washer, try turning the worn one the other way around, – but don't expect it to last long.

If you have a Continental tap, you may not be able to buy exact-size replacements. In this case buy the nearest Imperial size and trim the washer to fit with a Surform-type plane. ❞

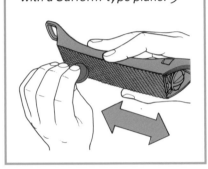

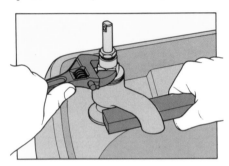

1 Remove the handle or loosen the shroud enough to get an adjustable spanner on the mechanism nut. Support the tap firmly, and unscrew.

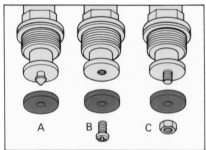

2 The washer could be a push fit (A), screwed to its jumper (B), or held by a small nut (C). Prise off or undo the old one and fit a replacement.

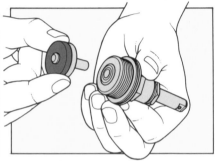

Alternatively, the washer may be combined with its jumper, which is a push-fit into the spindle. Use this type to replace a washer seized in its jumper.

REPAIRING SUPATAPS

You shouldn't need to turn the water off to rewasher a Supatap – but find out where to do it just in case. The temporary seal relies on a check valve dropping down from inside the tap when you unscrew the mechanism – so when you see the pin poke out, don't try to push it back in or you're likely to end up soaked!

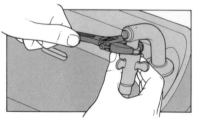

1 With the Supatap fully open, loosen the retaining nut using an adjustable spanner and unscrew the nozzle section from the body of the tap.

2 The washer is fitted to the anti-splash device inside the nozzle. Tap it out through the larger end and prise off the washer with a small screwdriver.

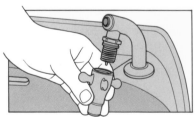

3 Fit an exact size replacement, refit the anti-splash device in the nozzle, and screw the nozzle back on the tap (water will spray as you do this).

CERAMIC DISC TAPS

Remove the cartridge as for a washered tap. Inside the cartridge are the two ceramic discs, one of which remains fixed while the other is turned across it to open the inlet.

Sometimes, the small lugs turning the movable disc wear down, allowing it to slip very slightly and leaving the inlet partly open. The only cure is to fit a complete new cartridge.

SERVICING TAPS

While rewashering, check the tap for leaks around the handle and shroud, and for binding.

Leaks are caused by wear in the spindle seals. Older type *rising* spindles are sealed with fibre packing; new type *non-rising* spindles have rubber 'O' ring seals.

On the old type, undo the *gland* nut on top of the mechanism (which governs the tightness of the spindle). Wind a few turns of PTFE tape around the spindle and poke it down into the body of the mechanism, then apply a smear of silicone gel and replace the nut. Try the tap:

if the spindle is too tight, loosen the nut a fraction; if it still leaks, tighten half a turn.

On the new type, hook out the circlip holding the spindle and withdraw it from below. Lever off the 'O' rings, smear on some silicone gel, and slide on the replacements.

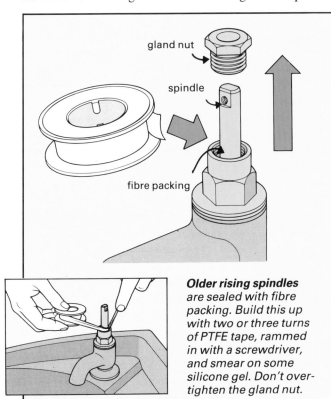

Older rising spindles are sealed with fibre packing. Build this up with two or three turns of PTFE tape, rammed in with a screwdriver, and smear on some silicone gel. Don't overtighten the gland nut.

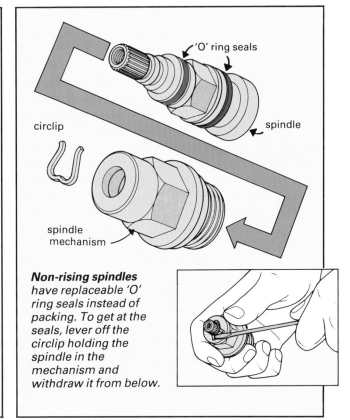

Non-rising spindles have replaceable 'O' ring seals instead of packing. To get at the seals, lever off the circlip holding the spindle in the mechanism and withdraw it from below.

MIXER TAP REPAIRS

Replacing the washers on washered mixer taps is the same as for pillar taps – they simply have two mechanisms within a single body.

Leaking swivel spout

Renewing the 'O' ring seals on a leaking swivel spout means removing the spout. It may be held by:

■ A small grub screw on the tap body which slots into a groove in the spout to lock it.

■ A screw-on shroud, underneath which is a circlip. Dig the circlip out with a small screwdriver or pliers.

■ A lug which passes through a slot in the tap body. Simply align the spout and body, then pull.

Replacing a diverter

There is no need to turn off the water to replace the diverter washer on a shower mixer.

In the most common design, the

washer is mounted on the end of the sprung-loaded diverter mechanism inside the tap body. To remove the mechanism, lift up the diverter knob or lever, get a small adjustable spanner on the flattened stem, and unscrew anti-clockwise.

The washer is attached to the mechanism like an ordinary tap washer. Remove it by undoing the retaining nut, fit a new one, then refit the diverter mechanism.

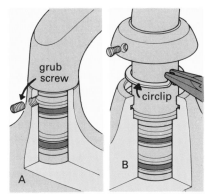
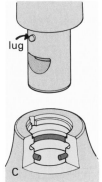
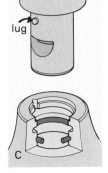
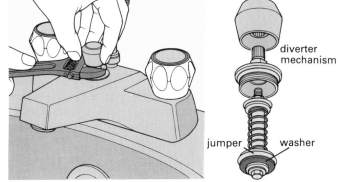

Mixer swivel spouts may be held by a grub screw (A), a circlip under a screw-on shroud (B), or a lug which you release by aligning the spout with the tap body (C).

Shower mixer diverter mechanisms screw into the body of the tap. The diverter washer is usually held in its jumper by a small nut or crosshead screw.

RESEATING A TAP

When a tap seat becomes worn, no amount of rewashering will stop it dripping. Nor is the problem only confined to old taps: new tap seats can wear prematurely if particles of grit or metal find their way into the mechanism. Either way, regrinding the seat is a lot easier and cheaper than replacing the taps. There are two ways to go about it.

Metal reseating tools can be hired with interchangeable cutters to suit ½″ and ¾″ taps.

Plastic reseating kits consist of a universal clip-together plastic tool, plus spare washers and a set of disposable abrasive grinding discs.

In both cases, check the seat first for signs of score marks. These will show up as black lines when you start grinding, but disappear as soon as the seat is properly ground-in. Make sure you don't over-grind.

Trade tip

No reseating tool?

6 *If you can't get hold of a reseating tool, there are two other things to try:*
Fit a Holdtite washer, which sits deeper inside the seat than an ordinary washer to compensate for any wear. The only drawback is that the tap must be turned more times to open and close it. The Holdtite washer comes with its own jumper, which has a peg that fits most tap mechanisms.

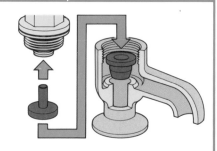

Fit a 'universal' plastic insert which comes in a kit to suit many older tap designs.
- Remove the tap mechanism as you would for rewashering.
- Push the insert into the seat with the flange uppermost.
- Exchange the old jumper and washer for the new ones supplied.
- Reassemble the tap, then open and close the tap a few times to push the new seat fully home. 9

1 *To use a metal tool,* fit the correct size cutter for the tap and screw it into the tap body. Adjust until you feel the cutter touch the seat.

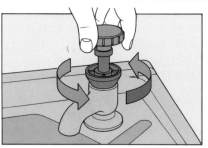

2 *Turn the handle a few times,* then remove the tool and check the effect. Repeat, checking frequently, until any score marks on the seat disappear.

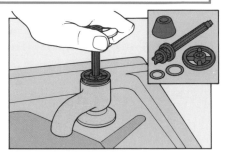

Plastic reseating tools can be used like metal ones, but have disposable grinding discs. To grind, push into the tap body and press down while turning.

PROBLEM SOLVER

Removing stubborn handles

If a tap handle proves difficult to remove, it's a good idea to try the other tap – you may be forcing the handle against a hidden screw.

Failing this, there are several things to try before resorting to brute force.

Plastic handles which screw on may have had the screw covers stuck down – try prising them up with a small screwdriver.

If you are sure they are the pull-off type, try tapping a pair of wooden wedges underneath to lift them off.

It's also possible that the handles have broken and been glued back on. In this case you have no choice but to break or saw them off and fit new ones.

Brass handles and shrouds are easily damaged; use a pair of slip-joint pliers (rather than

Mole grips) and wrap the jaws in a rag to avoid scratching.

If a handle remains stuck after you've removed the grub screw, wrap it with a cloth and pour on boiling water followed by cold. Alternatively, apply a squirt of penetrating oil, leave for an hour, and try again.

Another trick is to use the shroud to force off the head.
- Open the tap fully and undo the shroud.
- Place two small pieces of wood under either side so that you force the shroud against the handle.
- Close the tap in the normal way. As you do so, the handle should start to lift off.

If the shroud is stuck, you could try loosening it with a *chain wrench* – used by car mechanics to remove oil filters (remember to protect the chrome).

Use the shroud to force off a stubborn chromed brass handle.

Loosen a shroud with slip-joint pliers. Pad the jaws with cloth.

CLEARING BLOCKED TRAPS AND WASTES

Traps – sometimes called 'U' bends – are sections of waste pipe which remain permanently filled with water to stop smells filtering back through the drains. Every water-holding plumbing fitting has one, usually connected directly to the waste outlet, but sometimes further along the waste pipe itself.

Unfortunately, traps are also a natural place for waste particles to collect. Better design and the use of plastic have helped to make modern traps smoother – and therefore less likely to block – than the old metal type. But no amount of good design can eliminate the problem altogether. In the end, it's up to the user to be careful about what is washed down the drain – and that's easier said than done.

Even so, it pays to be aware of the kinds of things which cause trap blockages, not least because this knowledge can help you decide how to deal with the problem. The worst offenders, in order, are:
- Tea leaves and coffee grounds.
- Meat fats washed away with washing-up liquid.

The classic symptoms of a blocked trap. Clearing is messy rather than difficult.

- Food particles – rice, peelings.
- Household fillers and plaster.
- Hair (particularly in baths).

Often, it's possible to clear a trap without resorting to dismantling it (see *Shifting blockages* overleaf). But stubborn blockages and obstructions further down the waste pipe may call for more drastic action.

(see *Shifting blockages* overleaf)

Trade tip

Tell tale signs

❝ Blocked traps don't always occur suddenly – often there is a gradual build-up of debris which causes the water to drain away increasingly slowly. This is the time to act, before you have the added problem of getting rid of the waste water. ❞

TYPES OF TRAP

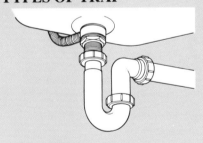

Plastic 'U' bends have an easy flow line, so are less likely to block – though if they do, they are quickly dismantled. The two sections are joined by threaded unions.

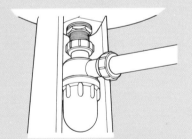

Plastic bottle traps are more compact than 'U' bends, making them the natural choice for basins. The lower half unscrews for clearing, or has a push-and-turn bayonet fitting.

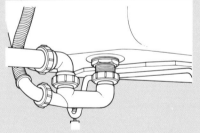

Low level bath traps are used where a deeper 'U' bend or bottle trap would be impossible to fit, and some models have an integral overflow. The horizontal section is prone to collect hair.

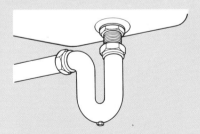

Metal 'U' bends of lead or copper are difficult to dismantle and so often have a small threaded clearing eye. Lead traps are easily damaged, and there's a risk of the eye snapping off.

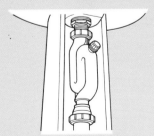

Straight-through traps are mostly found behind basin pedestals where space is limited. The tight bends are a natural place for blockages, so there is usually a clearing eye in the top.

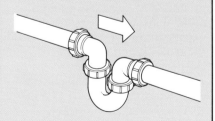

Running traps are mostly found in shower wastes where access beneath the tray is restricted. A common cause of blockages is that the trap is fitted the wrong way round.

SHIFTING BLOCKAGES

Most traps are easily dismantled, but gaining access to them is often more difficult. For this reason, it's always worth trying to clear the blockage by simpler means.

Plunging works best where there is a single appliance connected to the trap. Where there are several, such as a two-bowl kitchen sink with drainer hoses, it is less effective.

Poking with coathanger wire or a sink auger works well on 'U' bends, less so on bottle traps.

Burning with caustic soda is very effective on blockages caused by build-ups of grease – but the chemical itself is highly dangerous and must be used with care.

Caustic soda can damage old lead piping but won't harm plastic. Any water trapped in the fitting must be removed first (see Problem Solver).

CLEARING METAL TRAPS

Place a bucket or bowl under the trap to catch the contents.

■ Unscrew the clearing eye by gently tapping on one of the lugs with a hammer and bolster – or similar wide-bladed tool. If the eye is tight, arrange some means of support to avoid placing strain on the trap.

■ Hook out the obstruction with a piece of bent coathanger wire.

■ Wrap a few turns of PTFE tape around the thread of the eye before replacing it, and take care not to overtighten.

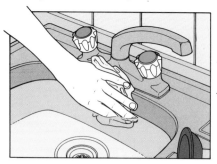

1 **Before plunging a trap**, block up the overflow with a wet rag and fill the fitting to overflow level. This helps to create a good pressure build-up.

2 Using the largest possible plunger, place it over the waste outlet and work it up and down vigorously to build up the force of the push-pull effect.

Trade tip

Making a plunger

❝ If you don't have a plunger, try using an old plastic ball cut in half – or at a pinch, a large saucepan lid. Simply pump up and down over the waste outlet in a rapid succession of short, sharp strokes. ❞

1 **To use a sink auger**, begin by feeding it down through the waste outlet into the trap. Turn the handle as you go to help the screw past the blockage.

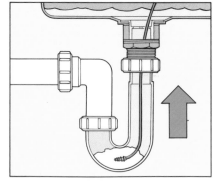

2 When you feel the auger move easily, withdraw it slowly turning the handle at the same time. With luck, the screw will carry the obstruction with it.

⚠ USING CHEMICALS

Caustic soda and other proprietary drain clearing products are extremely harmful to the skin, so always follow the manufacturer's instructions. Wear gloves and some form of eye protection when using caustic soda, and keep the tin out of the reach of children.

Also, never mix household cleaning products (for example, bleach and lavatory cleanser) in an attempt to clear a trap. Some combinations produce a gas which is, quite literally, lethal.

DISMANTLING PLASTIC TRAPS

Make sure the container you place under the trap is big enough to hold the contents of the sink or basin before you begin dismantling. See Problem Solver if there is no room to get a container underneath.

With the trap apart, you should be able to hook out the obstruction with coathanger wire. Take the opportunity to clear away any debris around the waste outlet.

Blockages in the waste pipe

If the blockage is further down the waste pipe, removing the trap should make it possible to reach it – either with a sink auger or coathanger wire. With upstairs fittings, check the hopper head too: this can easily become blocked with fallen leaves, resulting in the same symptoms as a blocked trap.

If all else fails, you could try using water pressure from a garden hose to shift the blockage. However, to conform with the water byelaws, this **must** have a double check valve fitted somewhere along its run to guard against back-siphonage. (You may be able to run it from an outside tap containing such a valve.) Pack the mouth of the pipe around the hose to build up pressure in the waste pipe. Few blockages will resist this method.

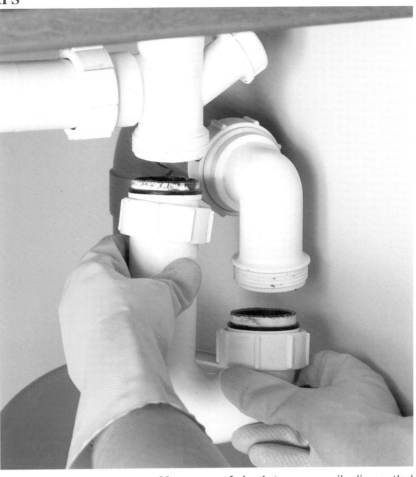

Most types of plastic trap are easily dismantled for clearing, but note which parts go where as you undo them and be sure to save the seals.

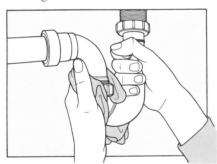

If a plastic nut is hard to undo, wrap a piece of rag around it to gain extra purchase, or wear a glove. Only use a wrench if all else fails.

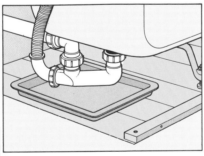

Remove the bath panel to gain access to a bath trap. Empty the bath, and place a tray or old towel under the trap to catch the remaining water.

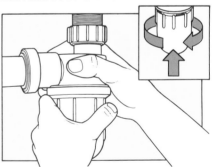

Bottle traps are the easiest to undo. Most types simply unscrew, but some newer designs have a bayonet fitting which must be pushed up and turned.

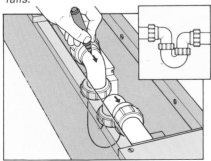

Running traps found on shower wastes may be some way from the actual tray. Mark the direction of flow on the side of the trap in pencil before dismantling.

Hopper head blockages sometimes produce the same symptoms as a blocked trap in a fitting upstairs. Hook out the debris and flush with a hose.

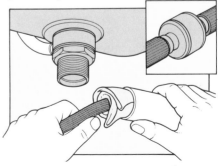

A hose used to flush a waste pipe blockage must have a double check valve fitted. Pack around the mouth of the pipe with a wet rag to build up the pressure.

REASSEMBLING THE TRAP

Take care not to damage the rubber seals or overtighten the nuts when reassembling a plastic trap. Silicone lubricant – as used to make push-fit joints on supply pipes – helps prevent damage to the seals.

If you find the trap leaks after refilling, don't tighten the nuts any further. Instead, dismantle the trap once more and check for the following faults:
- Grit in the seal.
- Old jointing compound – this attacks the plastic.
- Serious misalignment between the various pipes.
- Distortion of the waste pipe end.
- Pinched, cracked or broken seals.

Trade tip

Save the seals?

❝ Discard a seal which is obviously damaged. If a replacement is unavailable, improvise one from a good number of turns of PTFE tape; wrap this around the shoulder of the fitting, not around the thread. If the plastic nuts prove difficult to screw on, squirt a drop of washing up liquid on the threads. ❞

On some traps, the waste pipe simply pushes into the end of the trap. If possible, smear the ring seal with silicone lubricant to avoid damage during reassembly.

'Universal' screw-fit connections are now taking over from push-fit joints. Fit the rubber seal on the outside of the waste pipe, before inserting in the trap.

▐ PROBLEM SOLVER ▌

Siphoning out water

Where you're faced by a bathful of water to empty before using caustic soda or dismantling the trap, you'll find siphoning a lot quicker than baling with a bucket.
- Connect a garden hose to a nearby tap and turn it on for a few seconds to fill the hose with water.
- Keeping the hose filled, remove the tap end and plug it. Insert the other end in the bath and weight down near the waste outlet.
- Run the hose out of the window (or better, to a drain) below the level of the bath. Unplug the end and the water will siphon away.

Replacing a trap

A trap which is damaged or old and difficult to unblock is best replaced with a modern 'multifit' design. There are many different patterns, but the 'Universal' type can be adjusted to fit virtually any pipe/waste outlet position. Remember to buy the 32mm (1¼″) size for a basin waste, a 38mm (1½″) trap for other fittings.

Check before you start that the new trap will fit. If there is a gap to be made up between the trap and the existing waste pipe, buy a multifit push-fit connector and a length of the same-size plastic waste pipe.
- Sever the waste pipe as near to the old trap as possible using a

hacksaw.
- Unscrew the old trap with a large adjustable wrench.
- Fit the new trap on the waste pipe and screw to the outlet.

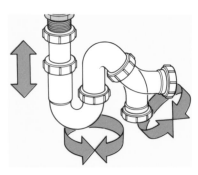

'Universal' replacement traps can be adjusted to fit almost any waste pipe/outlet layout.

Persistent blockages

If you have a complicated waste pipe run which is prone to regular blocking, it could be worth fitting an *access tee* to make clearing or auguring easier. As many waste pipes, particularly lead, are incompatible with certain fittings, it's safest to use a push-fit 'multifit' tee fitting such as the McAlpine 'VM'. The access branch can be sealed with a blank cap from the same range.

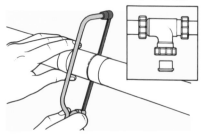

1 Position the tee so that it provides the best possible access to the problem section of waste pipe. Offer up the fitting, mark the pipe with tape, and cut with a fine toothed hacksaw.

2 Sand the cut pipe ends smooth, then slip on the nuts and sealing rings and jiggle on the tee. Hand-tighten the nuts, and fit the blanking cap on the access branch.

CLEARING BLOCKED DRAINS

The discovery of blocked drains is enough to send most people rushing for professional help. But providing you have a few simple pieces of equipment, clearing the blockage yourself is usually neither difficult nor particularly unpleasant. The secret is not to be daunted by the fact that drainage systems largely run underground – although you can't see them, their workings are deceptively simple.

Drains which are totally blocked and flooding over are the most unpleasant, so act promptly if you encounter any of the following:
- Abnormal gurgling sounds.
- 'Drain' smells inside the house.
- Overflowing gullies outside.
- Raised water levels in the WC.

Polypropylene drain rods provide an answer to most blockages.

.... Shopping List ....

Most blockages can be removed with a set of *polypropylene drain rods*, using one or other of the attachments shown below. Some sets include a selection of attachments as part of the kit; with others, you have to buy them as and when the need arises, which is less convenient.

Although you can hire them, drain rods are cheap enough to pay for themselves in a single job. They also have many other uses (see Tip). Don't, however, be tempted to buy an old set of wooden rods as these have a tendency to break.

Other equipment for unblocking drains which is useful to have available includes:
- Gloves and a face mask.
- A garden hose.
- A WC (cooper's) plunger. (This differs from the sink type in having a longer handle and a flat rubber disc for dealing with S-shaped WC traps.)
- A crowbar or spade for lifting manhole covers (see Problem Solver).

A sink or drain auger may also come in handy for some types of blockage, but is rarely essential.
Hiring tools should only be necessary for really stubborn blockages. You may need:
Powered augers for cutting through tree roots.
High pressure water jetting equipment for flushing drains.
Flexible drain rods on a drum for coping with very long drain runs.

Trade tip

Uses for drain rods

❝ One good reason for buying a set of drain rods is that they have plenty of other uses around the house – threading cables under floors, sweeping chimneys (with a brush attachment) and clearing leaves from rainwater pipes to name but a few. ❞

DRAIN ROD ATTACHMENTS

Rubber discs in 100mm and 150mm (4″ and 6‴) sizes to suit standard drain sizes. Used for plunging and clearing blocked gulleys, inaccessible runs and interceptors (see Problem Solver).

Worm screw for withdrawing roots and other fibrous blockages.

Small brush for degreasing and cleaning the inside of pipes.

Folding scraper for withdrawing silt and debris from the bottom of pipes.

Flexible wire leader for tight bends.

Wheel for overcoming tight bends and obstructions.

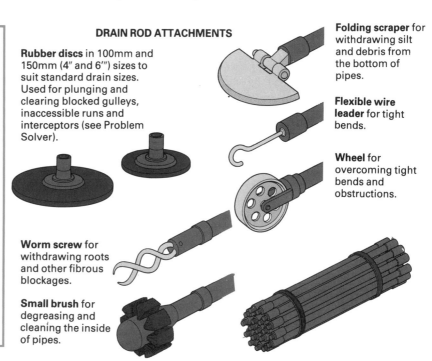

WHERE TO START

No matter how the drains run, there is a set procedure for dealing with blockages:

■ Establish that the problem isn't caused by a blocked appliance trap or waste pipe.

■ Lift the manhole (inspection chamber) cover nearest the house (see Problem Solver).

■ If the manhole is full of effluent, you know the blockage is downstream of this point. Start rodding here, away from the house.

If this doesn't work, move to the next manhole, If this is full too, rod the downstream end; otherwise, rod back up towards the full manhole to attack the blockage from the other side.

■ If the manhole is empty, you know the blockage is upstream. Get a helper to try various taps and appliances around the house while you watch the manhole to see which pipes are blocked. You can then rod the affected pipe.

Safe and clean

Never leave a manhole uncovered when you aren't there, and erect a makeshift barrier if you have to leave it unattended.

After clearing the blockage, flush all pipes and manholes with a hose. Wash all equipment in disinfectant and give yourself a good scrub-down.

Trade tip

Water power

❛ Don't underestimate the power of hydraulics – in this case the water trapped in the drain – to shift blockages. Often you can harness this power without much difficulty using only a couple of rods and a rubber disc attachment.

Push the rod assembly into the drain at any convenient point upstream of the blockage, then pump vigorously backwards and forwards. In many cases the pressure built up by the water already in the drain will be enough to clear the blockage. Make sure, though, that you hold on tightly to the rods, otherwise the suction effect created by the pumping will draw them down into the pipe. ❜

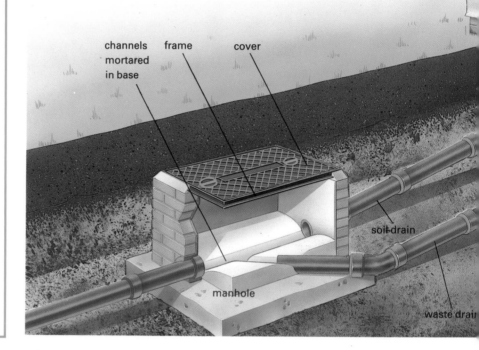

channels mortared in base — frame — cover — soil drain — manhole — waste drain

USING DRAIN RODS

If the blockage can't be cleared by pumping (see Tip), try physically shifting it using several rods screwed together. Which attachment you fit is largely a matter of trial and error, Start with a rubber disc unless you have reason to think the problem is caused by roots (in which case

fit an auger).

Keep turning the rods clockwise as you push them down into the drain, so that there's no risk of them unscrewing. When working without an attachment, count the rods down and count them back up again to double check that

none are left behind.

Full manholes

A manhole full of effluent is a daunting sight, but normally there's no need to empty it before rodding. You know that there is only one outlet hole, so just keep pushing the rods towards the downstream end.

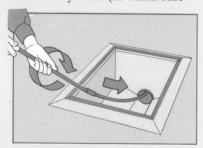

Keep turning rods in a clockwise direction all the time they are in the drain to stop them unscrewing. When you meet resistance, push and turn at the same time to dislodge the debris.

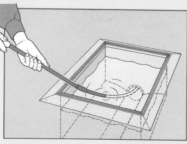

If the manhole is full, insert the rods 'blind' and push towards the downstream end. The channels mortared into the base of the manhole will guide the rods towards the outlet hole.

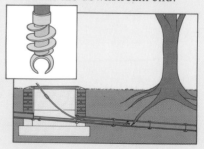

Tree roots won't respond to a rubber disc: fit a cutting attachment instead, or hire a purpose-designed root cutting auger which can be powered from an extension lead.

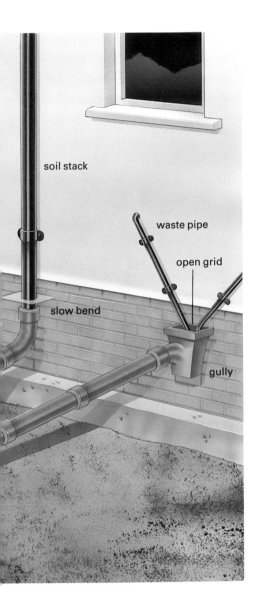

A typical drain layout, where the pipes from the external soil stack and waste gully meet at a manhole near the house. From here the drain could run to another manhole, or to the sewer.

(Labels on illustration: soil stack, waste pipe, open grid, slow bend, gully)

BLOCKED GULLIES AND STACKS

Gullies are notoriously prone to blockages, particularly the older open-grid type where leaves are often the problem. You can prevent this by covering the grid with wire mesh.

Blockages further down are usually caused by a build-up of silt, or by an accumulation of grease and food particles (especially from sinks). In this case, remove the cover or grid and reach into the gully to feel for the blockage; you may have to remove quite a lot of debris before the outlet hole clears.

There are two ways to deal with more serious blockages in the gully trap:
■ By plunging from the gully end using a cooper's plunger or drain rod with rubber disc.
■ By rodding up the pipe connecting the gully with the nearest manhole. (But take care not to force the blockage further into the gully trap.)

Soil pipes and combined soil/waste stacks rarely block on the vertical section – usually the trouble lies in the bend at the foot of the stack.

In most cases the blockage can be shifted by rodding back up from the nearest manhole, though as with a gully blockage you should take care not to compress it further into the stack. Alternatively, there may be a rodding eye or access trap in the stack itself, allowing you to insert a drain auger.

Failing this, it's possible to rod down the stack from the top – but only if you have safe access to the roof. It's best to consider this a last resort.

Waste pipes generally block at the hopper head or at the open end above the gully. Blockages can often be cleared by hand; if not, treat as for other stacks.

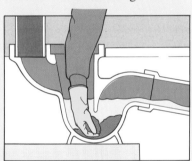  

Most gully blockages occur in the base of the gully or at the mouth of the trap. They are best shifted by hand, using stiff wire to break up any hard debris.

Stacks often have screw-on access traps or rodding eyes, allowing you to insert a wire or auger. If not, rod towards the stack from the nearest manhole.

WC BLOCKAGES

Like other appliances, WCs have traps which are prone to blocking. Often the cure is to pour down some bleach and leave for a while. If this doesn't work, try pouring in several buckets of water in quick succession – preferably from a height of around 1m (3′) to increase the momentum.

More stubborn blockages generally respond to plunging with a cooper's plunger – or failing this, a drain rod with rubber disc attachment. The only exceptions are syphonic WCs with double sealed traps; on these, use an auger instead.

 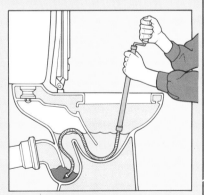

Most blockages in WC traps can be shifted using a cooper's plunger. Work it backwards and forwards vigorously in the mouth of the trap to bring hydraulic pressure to bear on the blockage.

Double sealed WC traps don't respond to plunging. If the blockage can't be shifted using bleach or by pouring in buckets of water, it must be cleared using a sink or drain auger.

Lifting manhole covers

Manhole covers are never easy to lift, but rust can make matters worse still. There are several things you can try:

■ Gently tap all the way around the edge with a heavy hammer or lump of wood.

■ Apply heat from a blowtorch around the edges to release the seal.

■ Apply penetrating oil to the edges and leave to work for several hours.

■ Use an old garden spade as a lever to lift the cover.

■ Thread ropes through the cross bars and around a stout length of timber, then lift with the aid of a helper (but check first that the bars haven't rusted through).

When replacing a cover, apply motor grease around the seal to prevent future jamming.

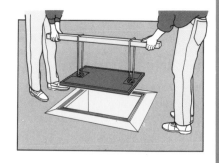

Covers with cross bar handles can often be shifted using rope and a piece of stout timber.

Hidden manhole covers

Manholes or smaller *clearing eyes* are supposed to be included wherever a drain branches or changes direction. Very few drains are laid without them, so if you can't find any covers the chances are they have been hidden – usually by garden outbuildings or loose-laid paving.

Larger and older properties may also have a manhole inside – often in the hallway. This should be the *double-sealed* type, with a screw-down cover.

The positions of hidden manholes can usually be fixed by taking the soil stack, gully and road as reference points: drains always run in straight lines between 'features' and you know that they must eventually converge towards a public sewer in the road. Bear in mind, though, that you may share a manhole with your neighbour – or even with several neighbours if you live on an estate served by a *private sewer*.

Another trick is to check where the manholes are in neighbouring properties – if the houses are identically built, you can assume that your own manholes are in the same place. And as a last resort, you could hire a metal detector to track down the covers.

Work out the position of a hidden manhole cover using other drain 'features' as reference points.

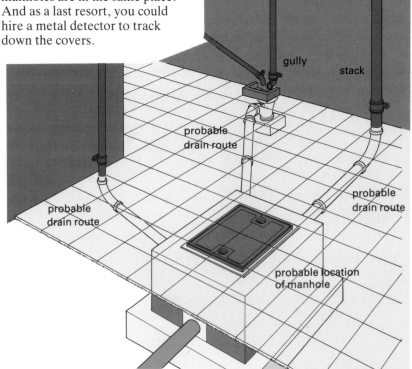

gully

stack

probable drain route

probable drain route

probable drain route

probable location of manhole

Blocked interceptors

An old fashioned method of providing a seal between the household drains and the public sewer was to place a U-shaped trap after the last manhole in the run. Known as *interceptors*, these are a common place for blockages to occur.

Usually the trap responds to rodding with a rubber disc attachment in the same way as any other manhole. If not, hook out the stopper covering the bypass pipe above the trap.

This should partially empty the manhole, allowing you to rod through both the bypass pipe and the main outlet. If this doesn't work, there are two possible causes of the problem.

■ The blockage is further down the run, possibly near the public sewer. In this case call in your local water undertaking, since the problem is likely to involve other properties connected to the same system.

■ The chain holding the stopper has rusted through, allowing the stopper to fall into the interceptor trap. In this case you should seek professional advice.

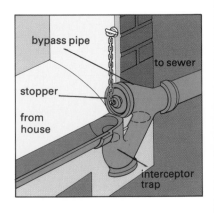

bypass pipe

to sewer

stopper

from house

interceptor trap

Interceptor traps have a bypass pipe running above them covered by an earthenware stopper.

REPAIRS TO WC CISTERNS

Niggling WC faults such as hit and miss flushing have a habit of turning into something more serious. Even so, there are surprisingly few problems that can't be fixed with just a few simple tools and the right spare part.

This section explains how flushing faults and leaks occur, and shows what can be done to fix them. Ball-valve problems are covered on pages 37-40.

How WCs work

WCs are far from complicated, but knowing how they work makes it much easier to trace and rectify faults.

A modern WC *cistern* is designed to deliver a measured quantity of water to flush the pan. This is done by storing the water in the cistern and then discharging it via a *siphon unit* operated by a lever or button. The siphon only works when the cistern is full, ensuring the right amount of water is delivered.

Flushing causes a *lifting plate* and *diaphragm* inside the siphon to rise, drawing water up and then down again into the flush pipe. From then on, the siphoning action takes over, bending the diaphragm upwards and drawing the rest of the water from the cistern into the flush pipe.

When the cistern empties, the siphoning action ceases, the

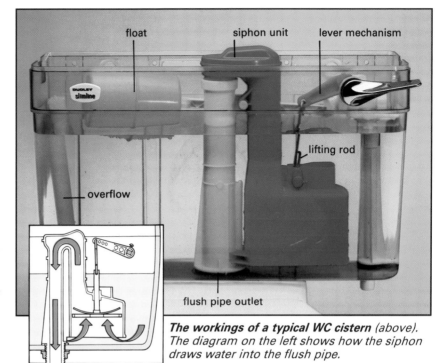

The workings of a typical WC cistern (above). The diagram on the left shows how the siphon draws water into the flush pipe.

diaphragm falls, and the ballvalve controlling the water inlet admits a fresh supply of water.

Variations on a theme

The description above applies to a *washdown* pan, in which the flushing water simply displaces the water in the pan trap. Modern washdown pans have a dual position siphon, to save water: pressing the lever or button and then releasing it delivers a

part-flush; holding the lever down delivers a full flush.

More sophisticated WCs work on the *siphonic principle* and usually incorporate a *double trap* pan. In this case, a *pressure reducing* ('puff') pipe attached to the siphon sucks air out of the chamber between the traps as the diaphragm in the cistern rises. This causes the pan contents to empty before the flushing water enters, giving quieter operation.

TYPES OF WC PAN AND CISTERN

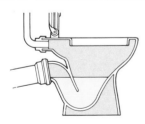

Washdown: the most common type, in which water from the cistern enters through the flush pipe and displaces the contents of the trap.

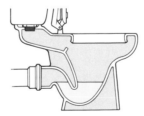

Single trap siphonic: the narrow trap outlet creates a partial vacuum which sucks out the contents as fresh water enters. Quieter in operation.

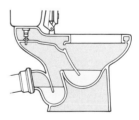

Double trap siphonic: flushing creates a vacuum in the chamber between the two traps, sucking out the contents silently as fresh water enters.

High level: the cistern and pan are connected by a long flush pipe – usually of metal, now sold as two-piece plastic.

Low level: the plastic cistern is connected to a separate pan via a length of plastic or metal flush pipe.

Close coupled: the ceramic cistern is joined directly to the pan, both being sold as a matching set.

FAULTFINDER CHART

SYMPTOM	POSSIBLE CAUSES	CURE
Poor or non-existent flushing; no feeling of resistance to flush lever or chain	■ Perished or damaged diaphragm washer ■ Broken lever arm linkage or pull chain arm linkage.	■ Renew diaphragm ■ Inspect mechanism; identify broken part and replace or temporarily repair
Poor flushing (siphonic WC)	■ The water in the pan does not draw away immediately the flush is activated but is only displaced by the new water coming in.	■ Replace the 'puff pipe' sealing washer
Resistance to flush action but only a small quantity of water enters the pan	■ Insufficient water in cistern ■ Damaged diaphragm ■ Blockage in flush pipe	■ Check water level; adjust ballvalve to suit ■ Check diaphragm ■ Check flushpipe
Leaks around cistern base or flush pipe connection	■ Perished seals on flush pipe joints.	■ Replace seals
Cistern continuously filling and emptying	■ Water coming in too fast.	■ Check ballvalve seating; restrict flow by adjusting stopcock.

NB An old-fashioned high level cistern and flushing mechanism may not be worth repairing, or you could have difficulty getting parts. See page 36 for how to replace it with a modern low-level type.

....Shopping List....

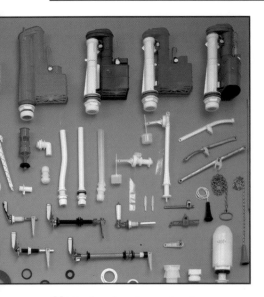

Most plumbers' merchants carry extensive ranges of parts for WCs.

As with other plumbing repairs, it's often difficult to buy replacement parts for WCs without first dismantling the mechanism concerned and then taking the part along to a plumbers' merchant to be matched. Note the make (and if possible the model) of the cistern.

This means thinking ahead: carry out repairs when you know the shops are open, and when the rest of the family won't be too upset by the water being turned off.

In an emergency, you can usually improvise something (ie stiff wire for the lever mechanism, or plastic sheet for a torn diaphragm), but short-term remedies are unlikely to stand much wear and tear.

Tools checklist: Adjustable wrench, slip-joint pliers, PTFE tape.

PERPETUAL FLUSHING
Perpetual flushing is a common condition in which water continues to enter the pan long after the WC has been flushed. It happens because the cistern fills too quickly, stopping the siphon from drawing in the air which halts the flushing sequence. Instead, the siphon and ballvalve work in perfect unison, filling and emptying at the same rate.

The answer is to slow down the filling rate of the ballvalve, either by fitting a High Pressure (HP) seat in the valve itself, or by turning the stopcock on the supply pipe to lower the water pressure.

FLUSHING PROBLEMS 1 – BROKEN LEVER MECHANISM

The weak link in a flush lever mechanism is the 'S' or 'C' hook connecting the lever arm, or push button, with the diaphragm lifting plate rod on the top of the siphon unit. New hooks are readily available from plumbers' merchants in various lengths, and in an emergency you can improvise with a piece of coathanger wire.

Breakages elsewhere in the linkage are rare, but it should be obvious how the bits go together if you need to remove them. One point to check is that a lever arm hasn't come loose from the cistern; if it has, retighten the backnut.

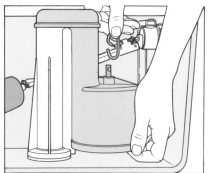

1 *If the hook has disintegrated and the rod is 'lost' inside the siphon, reach underneath the siphon unit and push up the diaphragm to reveal it.*

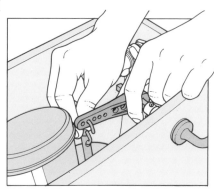

2 *On most mechanisms, the hook can be 'fiddled' straight on to the rod and lever. Sometimes, however, you need to unscrew the lever arm first.*

FLUSHING PROBLEMS 2 – SIPHON FAULTS

The most common siphon fault is a perished or torn diaphragm, but it's also possible for the siphon housing itself to have cracked.

In both cases the first step is to turn off the water supply to the cistern, then flush it to empty the contents. Bale out any remaining water or soak it up with a sponge.

Next, you must unscrew and remove the siphon unit.

On a separate cistern, you can do this without removing the cistern itself.

On a close coupled cistern, the cistern must be disconnected and unscrewed from the wall, then lifted clear of the pan so that you gain access to the siphon securing nut (see below). On a siphonic WC, it's also worth checking the seal around the 'puff pipe' which creates the vacuum between the pan traps; if this is perished or out of position, the proper flushing action will be disrupted.

Check the siphon unit body carefully for signs of cracking before reassembling the parts.

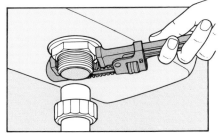

1 *On a separate cistern, unscrew the flush pipe coupling nut, then use a large wrench or slip-joint pliers to undo the siphon nut above.*

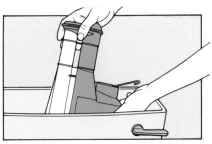

2 *Lift up the siphon clear of the cistern and uncouple the hook on top of the lifting rod. You may need to remove the ballvalve float arm to clear it.*

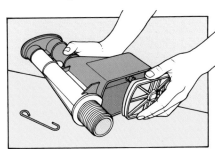

3 *Slide off the lifting rod washers, noting their order, and put them to one side. Then slide the rod and plate out of the bottom of the siphon housing.*

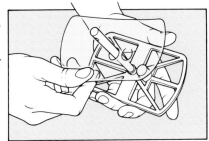

4 *Remove the worn out diaphragm and draw round it to make a paper pattern. Buy a new diaphragm the same size, then reassemble in reverse order.*

REMOVING CLOSE COUPLED CISTERNS

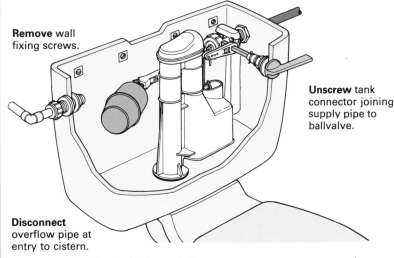

Remove wall fixing screws.

Unscrew tank connector joining supply pipe to ballvalve.

Disconnect overflow pipe at entry to cistern.

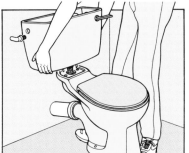

Lift off the disconnected cistern to gain access to the siphon nut and, on a siphonic pan, the seal around the 'puff pipe' passing down into the pan.

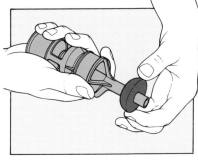

On a siphonic pan, check the seal around the 'puff pipe'. Fit a new one so that it is pushed up, as the cistern is replaced, to sit over the hole in the pan.

Trade tip

Check the flush pipe

If the diaphragm turns out to be broken, you can virtually guarantee that the rest of it is blocking the flush pipe or the flush ways in the pan. Blockages at other times are likely to be caused by foreign bodies – for example, parts of an old disinfectant dispenser.

If you can't see all the way round the flush pipe, drop a small nut on the end of a piece of string down the pipe, then use the string to drag through a small piece of rag.

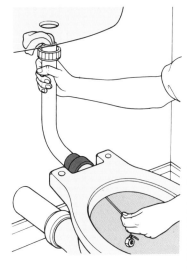

CURING LEAKS

Leaks can happen anywhere around a WC cistern, but they are most likely to occur after carrying out repair work.

Make a point of checking every washer and seal for wear as you remove it – it is false economy not to replace one which is obviously worn.

Doughnut washer – seals a close coupled cistern to the pan.

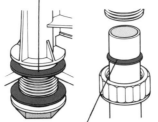

Siphon sealing washer to cistern – made of flat or stepped rubber.

Flush pipe top washer – could be flat, or a chamfered compression type. Seal the joint with the siphon; patch temporarily with PTFE tape.

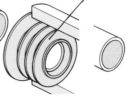

Internal flush cone – a butyl rubber or polythene push-fit fitting suitable for the new European standard WC with horizontal outlet.

Universal flush cone – a push-fit fitting which turns inside out to fit 1¼" or 1½" flush pipes. Slip a new cone on the flush pipe first.

CONVERTING A CISTERN

Converting from an obsolete high level cistern to a modern low level one may be a necessity if you can't get the parts you want. For convenience, choose a slimline plastic cistern which only requires around 150mm (6") between the wall and pan. There should also be around 600mm (24") clearance between the new cistern and the base of the pan.

Most cisterns are sold complete with siphon, lever mechanisms, ballvalve and overflow outlet. In addition you'll need a new plastic flush pipe and cone fitting, plus materials to re-route the overflow and supply pipes.

If you find later that the seat won't stay back, you can also buy cranked seat hinge fittings that bring it forward as it is raised.

Doing the conversion

Start by isolating the water supply, then disconnect and remove the old supply pipe and flush pipe; if they are badly corroded, you may have to saw through them. Afterwards, remove any screws holding the old cistern to the wall, and carefully lift it off its brackets.

The manufacturer's instructions should specify maximum/minimum heights for fitting the new cistern, so

position it first, then trim the new flush pipe to suit. You'll find it easier to assemble the siphon and other parts before fitting.

Fit the flush pipe with the new cistern in place, then adapt the supply and overflow connections. The new cistern will probably offer a choice of entry positions – side or bottom – so drill out the appropriate blanking holes.

Running in the supply should be a simple matter of rerouting the pipe. To run the overflow, you'll probably have to make a new hole in the outside wall, then seal around the pipe with mastic.

WHAT'S INVOLVED

Saw through old supply, overflow and fish pipe connections which are corroded.

New cistern screws to wall. Assemble siphon, ballvalve and other parts before fitting.

New overflow – run in 19mm uPVC pipe with solvent weld joints. Use a special threaded connector at the cistern.

Check clearance behind and above pan. Slimline cisterns need around 150mm (6").

You may have a choice of side or bottom entry for the water supply and overflow connections. Bottom entry means fitting standpipes inside the cistern.

Supply pipe – reroute in copper or plastic, finishing with a tap connector for connection to the ballvalve.

New flush pipe – buy oversize then trim to fit. Fit to pan using new flush cone.

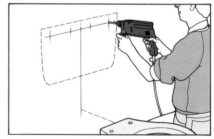

Mark a vertical line from the pan to centre the cistern, then draw a horizontal line to show where to drill and plug the wall. Screw the assembled cistern in place.

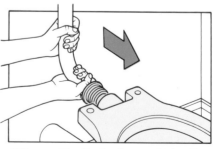

Offer up the flush pipe and trim if necessary. Fit the top to the siphon unit, then work on the flush cone and fit the lower end to the pan inlet.

REPAIRING BALLVALVES

Float-operated valves – ballvalves – are the simple devices that control the flow of water into cold storage tanks, central heating feed and expansion tanks, and WC cisterns. Like taps, they are in more or less constant use, so it's not surprising that problems sometimes occur.

Check the chart shown below for symptoms of faults and their likely causes. Leaking overflows need urgent attention, since what starts as a tell-tale drip can quickly develop into a flood – most overflows can't cope with a full-scale flow of water (strictly speaking they are only *warning* pipes). The leak may also give rise to damp problems on the wall below.

Before you start a repair, identify what sort of valve you are dealing with (see below) and make sure that the shops are open – you may have to take the valve with you to get replacement parts. Don't forget that the water will have to stay off in the meantime.

IDENTIFYING BALLVALVE FAULTS

SYMPTOM	POSSIBLE CAUSES	CURE
Valve lets water by, causing overflow	■ Washer/diaphragm worn	■ Service valve
	■ Seat cracked by frost	■ Service valve
	■ Valve mechanism jammed due to scale	■ Service valve or replace
	■ Leaking float	■ Empty float and seal or replace
	■ Valve corroded due to dezincification	■ Replace valve with dezincification-resistant type
Valve won't let water by, causing tank to empty	■ Valve jammed due to lack of use (very common on C.H. feed and expansion tanks)	■ Service valve
Tank slow to fill	■ Valve outlet blocked with grit	■ Service valve
	■ Wrong seat or valve	■ Replace seat or valve
Excessive noise from valve as tank fills	■ Wrong seat or valve	■ Replace seat or valve
	■ Worn valve	■ Service or renew valve
	■ Water hammer due to high pressure	■ Turn down pressure or fit different valve
	■ Float bouncing on surface of water	■ Fit damper to float

TYPES OF BALLVALVE

All ballvalves work on the same basic principle: an air-filled float, attached to the valve via an arm, rises and falls with the water level in the tank.

Attached to the arm inside the valve is a plunger and plastic diaphragm (diaphragm type), or a piston with rubber washer (piston type), which closes off the water supply when the level is at the right height.

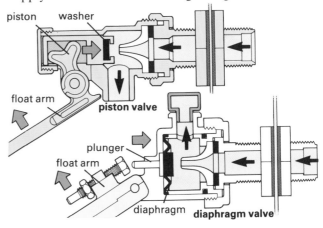

'Portsmouth' (piston type). For many years the standard valve on both tanks and WCs. Older all-brass versions are still common; newer models have a plastic piston and seating which is less prone to scale build-up. The Water Byelaws now ban Portsmouth valves from new installations.

'Croydon' (piston type) Rare, and now obsolete. Replace with a newer type if faulty.

'Brass Equilibrium' (piston type). Similar to the Portsmouth, but with an extra chamber that balances the force of the water pressure rather like a canal lock – resulting in quiet, smooth operation. Used in areas with abnormally high or variable water pressure.

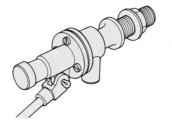

'Garston' (diaphragm type). Scale-resistant valve, usually plastic but sometimes brass, which has no moving parts in contact with the water. No tools needed for servicing.

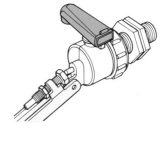

'New Brass Diaphragm' (diaphragm type – BS 1212 part 2). Similar in operation to the Garston, but with its water outlet mounted above the valve to eliminate the risk of back-siphonage.

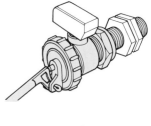

'Torbeck' (diaphragm type). A patented plastic valve for WC cisterns. It has a built-in damper and a collapsible underwater outlet which permits silent filling without risk of back-siphonage. ('Silent filling' tubes on ordinary valves are banned under the Water Byelaws).

SERVICING BALLVALVES

Most ballvalves can be dismantled for cleaning and servicing, leaving the tail and supply pipe connection undisturbed. This is always preferable, especially if the supply pipe is lead, but it's not worth trying to service a very old or badly scaled-up valve – replace it instead as described overleaf.

New parts – washers, seats, floats – are widely and cheaply available from DIY stores or plumber's merchants. But as with taps, you may need to take the old parts with you.

The first step is to turn off the water supplying the valve at the nearest stopcock. Check the water has stopped flowing by pressing down on the float arm.

When unscrewing the valve body, take care not to let it turn or you'll break the seal on the tank/WC cistern and strain the supply pipe connection.

Tools and materials: Adjustable spanner, wrench, self-locking wrench, small screwdriver, pliers, PTFE tape.

SERVICING A PISTON VALVE

After removing the working part of the valve (see step below), dismantle it following the diagram.

■ Remove the split pin and unscrew the end cap, then wiggle out the float arm and slide out the piston.

■ Hold the piston with a screwdriver and unscrew the end. (Newer pistons are in one piece.)

■ Dig out the old washer; replace it

SERVICING A PISTON VALVE

After removing the working part of the valve (see step below), dismantle it following the diagram.

■ Remove the split pin and unscrew the end cap, then wiggle out the float arm and slide out the piston.

■ Hold the piston with a screwdriver and unscrew the end. (Newer pistons are in one piece.)

■ Dig out the old washer; replace it with an identical size and type.

■ Replace the seating with one of the same size and pressure rating if it looks worn or is cracked.

■ Scour off any scale, then give the piston and body a thorough clean with metal polish.

■ Before reassembling, check the condition of the union washer and replace if necessary.

Trade tip

Pressure points

❛ Most newer ballvalves have replaceable seats with the outlet holes sized according to the pressure of the water passing through them.
Low pressure seats are for WC cisterns fed from storage tanks.
High pressure seats are for storage tanks and WC cisterns fed direct from the mains.

You can also get **full-way** seats for WC cisterns that fill painfully slowly because the storage tank is too low-down in the house to provide the normal amount of pressure.

Always specify what pressure rating you want when buying new parts or a new valve. Armed with this information, you can also cure a valve that fills too slowly or quickly (and thus noisily) simply by changing the seat accordingly. ❜

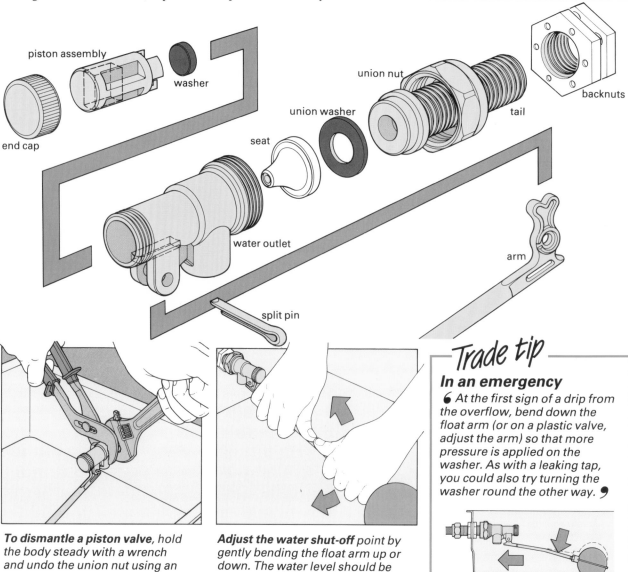

piston assembly | washer | end cap | seat | union washer | union nut | tail | backnuts | water outlet | arm | split pin

To dismantle a piston valve, hold the body steady with a wrench and undo the union nut using an adjustable spanner. Remove to a bench.

Adjust the water shut-off point by gently bending the float arm up or down. The water level should be about 25mm (1") below the overflow outlet.

Trade tip

In an emergency

❛ At the first sign of a drip from the overflow, bend down the float arm (or on a plastic valve, adjust the arm) so that more pressure is applied on the washer. As with a leaking tap, you could also try turning the washer round the other way. ❜

SERVICING A DIAPHRAGM VALVE

■ On most diaphragm valves, the diaphragm is immediately behind the retaining nut (see diagram). But on one type the nut is in the middle of the valve (inset), and you have to slide out a cartridge to expose the diaphragm. In this case, take care not to damage the sealing washer behind the seat.

■ Dig out the diaphragm with a flat-bladed screwdriver and check that the seat is in good condition.
■ The new diaphragm only fits one way, so check the old one to see which side was marked by the seat.
■ Reassemble the valve and screw the retaining nut back on by hand. Turn on water and test immediately.

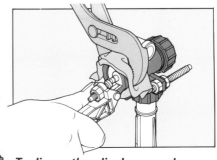

To dismantle a diaphragm valve, simply unscrew the retaining nut (if it is stiff, loosen it using an adjustable wrench with padding in the jaws).

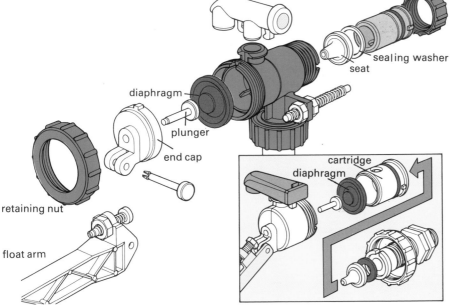

diaphragm
plunger
end cap
retaining nut
float arm

seat
sealing washer

cartridge
diaphragm

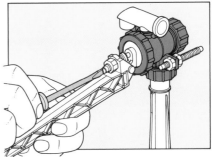

Adjust the water level by loosening the locknuts on the adjuster and screwing it in or out. Re-adjust when the washer has bedded in.

SERVICING A TORBECK VALVE

A constant drip from the front of the valve during filling is normal, but if you suspect the diaphragm needs replacing:
■ Unscrew the front of the valve body.
■ Dig out the diaphragm and clean in soapy water. It could be that this cures the problem; if not, replace the diaphragm.
■ Replace the diaphragm with the white spike pointing towards the valve. Position the bush on the outer edge of the diaphragm on the

steel pin fixed to the valve body.
■ Replace the front cover, checking that the float arm engages on the plastic pins.
■ Adjust the water level by altering the position of the float on the arm.
  Instead of different size seatings the Torbeck valve comes with a choice of flow restrictors for high and medium pressure. But if the valve takes more than 20 seconds to fill, it's more likely that the filter is blocked so check this first. (Early models may not have a filter.)

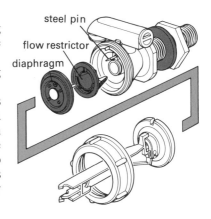

steel pin
flow restrictor
diaphragm

CURING FLOAT PROBLEMS

■ If the float develops a leak, the valve won't shut off at the correct point. Unscrew the float, empty out the water, and patch the hole with epoxy putty or tie a plastic bag over it. Replace as soon as possible.
■ Sometimes – and especially on Portsmouth valves – the float bounces on the ripples as the tank fills, causing water hammer in the supply pipe. You can cure this by fitting a purpose-made damper to the float arm. Alternatively, hang a punctured yoghurt carton in the tank,

suspended from the float arm by a length of galvanized wire.
■ In a WC cistern, the float may catch on the flushing mechanism causing the valve to jam open. If

necessary bend a brass arm so that the float is free to move throughout its travel; plastic arms generally have a choice of fitting positions.

Fit a damper – proprietary or home-made – to the float arm to stop the float bouncing.

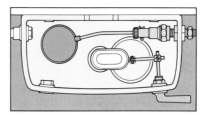

On a WC cistern, make sure the float doesn't jam – bend the arm or reposition the float to clear.

REPLACING A VALVE

New ballvalves aren't expensive, so if you can't get the parts to repair the old one (or it isn't worth repairing) then buy a matching replacement. Replacing the entire valve is likely to cause problems, so aim to 'graft' the working part of the new one on to the tail of the old one so that you don't have to disturb the supply pipe. Make sure you fit a new sealing washer where the two halves join.

If you have to replace the entire valve, or you are changing it for another type:

■ Try to ensure the new valve has the same length tail as the old one; if not, you may have to modify the supply pipe (see Problem Solver).

■ On a WC cistern, the length of the float arm may also be critical (though you can probably swap over the old one).

■ Specify whether the valve is for high pressure or low pressure application (see page 38).

■ If you live in a water area where dezincification is a problem, make sure the valve is plastic, or has a **DR** mark, indicating that it is dezincification-resistant.

Before you start, apply some penetrating oil to the connector nut and valve backnuts. Then, after turning off the water, open a tap lower down in the system to drain any water left in the supply pipe.

New valves are often supplied with self-sealing nylon backnuts which don't need washers, but make sure the area around the nuts is clean and free of old jointing compound so that the seals are watertight. On a WC, don't over-tighten the nuts.

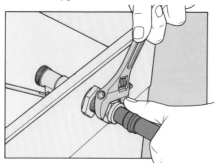

1 Taking care to support the supply pipe, undo the tap connector nut linking it to the valve tail. Pull the joint apart and gently ease the pipe away.

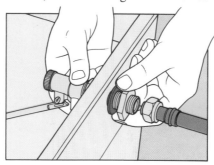

2 Using slip-joint pliers and an adjustable wrench, loosen the backnuts holding the old valve in place. Unscrew the outer backnut and lift away the old valve.

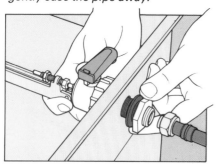

3 Fit the new valve in place, not forgetting any sealing washers, and screw on the outer backnut. Hold the valve upright as you tighten it.

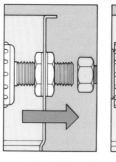

4 Check that the supply pipe fits the valve tail, and if necessary adjust the backnuts. Fit a new fibre washer and retighten the connector nut.

Trade tip

Valves with standpipes

❛ Some modern WCs require a bottom entry valve, which includes an integral standpipe. Valve operation is identical to the usual side-entry type.

If you're fitting an identical replacement, you should be able to leave the standpipe in place and simply undo the valve at the union. Otherwise, be sure to quote the length of the standpipe when ordering a new valve. ❜

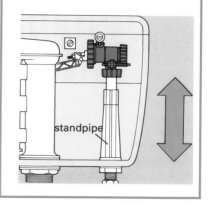

standpipe

PROBLEM SOLVER

Bridging the gap

If you can't get a new valve to match up to the existing supply pipe, don't force the pipe – it may cause the joint to leak, or weaken others along the run.

Normally, adjusting the positions of the backnuts on the valve tail gives you enough room to manoeuvre. Failing this, you may find that a screw-on *tap shank adaptor* is long enough to bridge the gap. Otherwise, you have no option but to saw off the old tap connector and fit a new one, together with a new section of pipe.

Persistent valve problems

The Keraflo valve is a patented design which uses ceramic discs instead of washers to shut off the water. It is only made to fit WC cisterns, but is claimed to be maintenance free and very reliable.

The valve comes in a basic unit to which you add a side entry connector or a separate standpipe for bottom entry. The fitting procedure is the same as for other ballvalves, but you may need an extending arm if the flushing handle restricts the float travel.

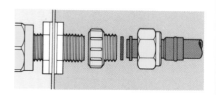

You may be able to bridge a small gap using a tap shank adaptor.

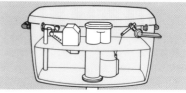

The Keraflo ceramic disc ballvalve for fitting to WCs.

CHANGING KITCHEN TAPS

Fitting new kitchen taps is one of the simplest of all plumbing jobs. Perhaps you want a change of style – new taps can give a whole new look to an old sink. Or maybe you just want to improve efficiency – modern taps turn on and off more easily than old ones, and are less likely to wear out or drip. Some models also come equipped with useful accessories such as swivel nozzles and rinsing sprays to make lighter work of the washing up.

This section assumes that your existing sink is in good condition and is already fitted with a set of taps. It doesn't matter whether the taps are sound or not, so long as the pipework is in good order. Bath and washbasin taps are often fitted in a similar way, but there are several important differences, so these are covered in detail on pages 45-48.

....Shopping List....

Important note: Tap fittings vary widely – run through the instructions overleaf, then make a list of what you need using the chart below.

YOU WANT	YOU NEED	YOU MIGHT NEED
Pillar taps	■ a pair of taps ■ suitable holes in worktop or sink ■ top-hat washers ■ adjustable spanner or tap tool* ■ tap connectors	■ anti-rotational washers ■ top-hat backnut ■ shank adaptor ■ penetrating oil ■ PTFE tape ■ sealing compound ■ junior hacksaw
A two-hole mixer	■ tap unit ■ two holes in sink or worktop ■ top-hat washers ■ adjustable spanner or tap tool*	■ top-hat backnut ■ shank adaptor ■ penetrating oil ■ PTFE tape ■ sealing compound ■ junior hacksaw
A monobloc mixer	■ tap unit ■ one hole in sink or worktop ■ reducing connectors ■ adjustable spanner or tap tool*	■ blanking plug in stainless steel, plastic or ceramic to conceal spare holes in two hole sink or worktop ■ penetrating oil ■ PTFE tape ■ sealing compound ■ junior hacksaw ■ hole saw attachment for electric drill

Traditional pillar taps

Versatile two-hole mixer (above)
Stylish monobloc mixer (below)

* A tap tool or old-style basin spanner is essential for loosening and tightening awkwardly placed tap backnuts. Tap tools are the better buy, since they double as ordinary spanners as well.

HOW TAPS FIT

Each of the three main types of kitchen tap – pillar taps, two-hole mixers and monobloc mixers – fits in a slightly different way, and your choice may also be influenced by what type of sink you have.

Pillar taps are usually cheapest. They come in pairs for hot and cold, so can't be used with double bowl sinks. Don't confuse with wash-basin taps – kitchen taps are taller to give room for saucepans and buckets.

Two-hole mixers fit into the standard holes in a sink unit. They are medium-priced and because of their swivelling spout may be more convenient than pillar taps.

Monobloc (single-hole) mixers are stylish, but usually expensive.

■ Swapping for a similar type of tap is normally simple, but you may need an adaptor as shown opposite.
■ Pillar and two-hole mixer taps are normally interchangeable, but pillar taps fitted through the worktop may be at the wrong spacing for a mixer.
■ A monobloc mixer may need a new, larger hole. The existing holes can be covered with blanking plugs.

Pillar taps *fitted through standard sink holes are held by a backnut and top-hat washer. When fitted through a thick worktop, a top-hat backnut is used instead.*

top-hat backnut

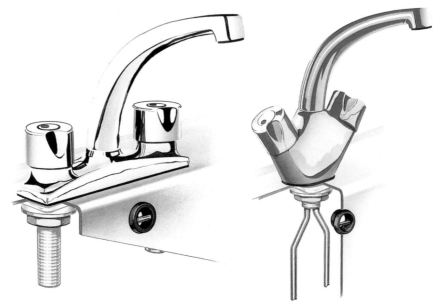

Two-hole mixer taps *fit through standard-spaced holes in sinks.*

Monobloc (single-hole) mixers *need a single, larger hole.*

REMOVING OLD TAPS

Before doing anything else, turn off your boiler or immersion heater and then turn off the water supply.

Most kitchen cold taps are fed on a branch from the rising main which should be equipped with its own stopcock. If not, isolate the supply at the main stopcock. If the hot supply has no stopcock of its own, isolate it at the gatevalve on the cold feed to the hot water cylinder or water heater.

Turn the taps on to drain the pipes and then, working beneath the sink, use a tap tool, spanner or adjustable wrench to undo the nut connecting the supply pipe to the tap tail. An old towel wrapped around the pipe will absorb any dribbles of water left in it.

Next, undo the backnut which secures the tap in place against the sink or worktop. If the tap itself turns while removing the backnut, hold it in place using an offcut of wood as a lever.

With the backnut removed, lift the old tap away and repeat the procedure for the other tap. Scrape away any remains of sealing compound or old gasket, taking care not to scratch the surface.

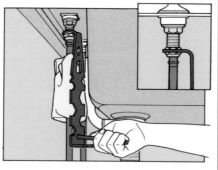

1 *Wrap some cloth around the pipes to catch any drips. Undo the tap connectors using the appropriate notch in a tap tool or an adjustable spanner.*

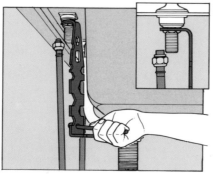

2 *The backnut is more difficult to reach and needs a tap tool or basin spanner to undo it. You may need to feel your way to lock the tool on the nut.*

Trade tip

Hold it steady

❝ *If the tap simply revolves with the backnut, I wedge it from above with a length of wood or wrap it in a cloth and grip it with pliers.* ❞

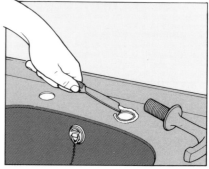

3 *Lift the tap away, including its washers. Scrape away any deposits of old sealing compound or gasket to ensure a watertight fit for the new tap.*

CONNECTION OPTIONS

The threaded **tails** of the taps are joined to the supply with screw-on **tap connectors** (except for monoblocs, which are connected direct). There are five options:

1 The new taps fit straight on to the old connectors.

2 Metric taps are about 12mm (½″) shorter than old Imperial ones. If the connectors won't reach there is a special fitting called a **shank adaptor** to extend the tail.

3 If the tails are completely out of alignment, use a **bendable tap connector kit** with hand-bendable copper pipe to span the gap.

4 Plastic taps are sometimes supplied with **plastic tap connectors** to make joints to copper pipe without damaging the fragile tails.

5 Monobloc taps may have bendable 10mm (⅜″) inlet pipes. To connect these to normal 15mm (½″) supply pipes, use **reducing connectors**.

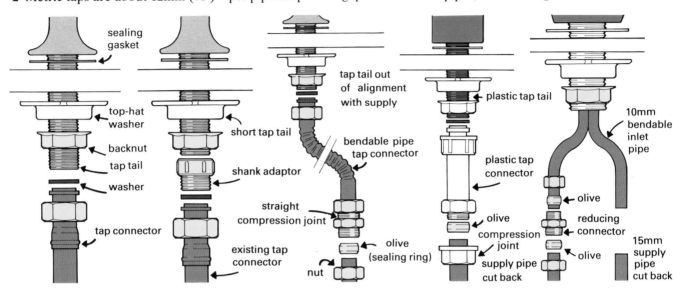

A tap connector with fibre sealing washer is standard.

Shank adaptors are used to bridge a small gap.

Bendable pipe tap connector kits span awkward gaps.

Plastic connectors are used with some plastic taps.

Reducing connectors join 10mm inlets to 15mm supply pipes.

ADAPTING CONNECTIONS

Test-fit the new taps to see how the pipes align. If you need a larger hole for a monobloc mixer, drill one with a hole saw and fit blanking plugs to the old holes.

■ If the taps fit the old connectors direct, or via a shank adaptor, continue as shown overleaf.

■ If you have to use flexible connectors, plastic connectors or reducing connectors (see above), the supply pipes must be cut back and the connectors joined to them. The easiest way to make the joints is via standard compression fittings.

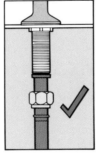 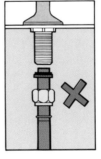

1 Hold the new tap in place to gauge whether you can connect it to the supply pipe without adjustment. Don't bother to fit the backnut at this stage.

2 If you need to adapt the supply, hand tighten the new fitting (in this case a plastic connector) on to the tap so you can mark where to cut the pipe.

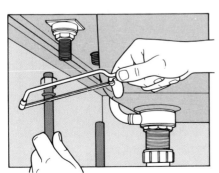

3 Cut the pipe squarely with a junior hacksaw. If necessary, pull the pipe out of its clips and hold a block of wood behind it to keep it steady.

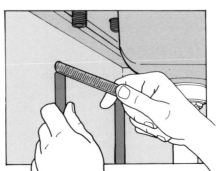

4 Remove any burrs from the cut end using a small file or old knife so that you can slip the new fitting in place without damaging it or the pipe.

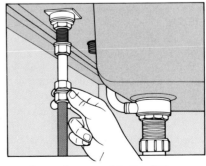

5 Loosely assemble the fitting to check that it aligns properly. Fit the nut, then the olive, and push the fitting down on to the end of the pipe.

CONNECTING THE TAPS

Fitting the new taps is virtually the reverse of removing the old ones once you have adapted the connections, but watch these points:

■ Make sure any sealing washers or gaskets supplied are fitted in their correct order before you fit the taps through the sink top.

■ If the taps turn too easily in their holes, fit **anti-rotational washers** from below.

■ On a thin sink, fit top-hat washers, followed by the backnuts. On thick worktops, fit special top-hat backnuts instead.

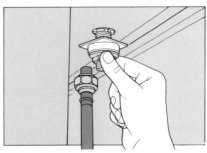

Fit the tap in place, including any washers, and screw the backnut on from underneath. Tighten the backnut firmly and check that the tap doesn't turn.

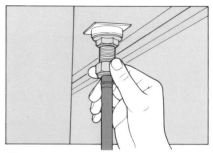

If you're reusing the old tap connector fit a new sealing washer. The connector should push into the tail as you insert the tap. Tighten the nut fully.

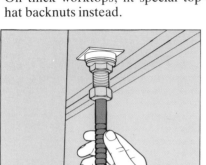

If you are using an adaptor, fit it to the tap tail and tighten the nut fully. Don't forget the sealing washer inside the actual tap connection . . .

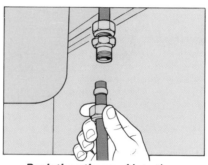

. . . Push the other end into the supply pipe after first slipping on a nut and olive. Slide the joint together and tighten the nuts 1½ turns above hand-tight.

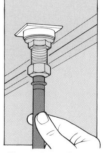

Turn the relevant stopcock back on and feel the connections for signs of leaks. If all is well, turn the tap on to make sure it works properly.

■ PROBLEM SOLVER ■

If it won't unscrew

Old joints may be difficult to undo because of corrosion and the difficulty of getting enough leverage on a nut which is concealed behind the sink. If the nut won't turn reasonably easily, don't force it. There are two things you can try:

Apply penetrating oil Use a spray can of the type with a long extension tube so you can reach up behind the sink. Leave it to soak in for at least 10 minutes.

Apply heat. Warm the joint with a hot air gun or blowlamp (unless the tap or nut is plastic), let it cool, then try again.

Old joints can be tough to undo. Apply penetrating oil and leave for 10 minutes, or heat the joint, let it cool for a while and then try again.

If it leaks

Leaks from the joints are most likely to be because they are not fully tightened. Try tightening the nuts a fraction to see if this cures the problem.

If it doesn't, turn the water off again and undo the joint.

With tap connectors, check that the washer is in place and intact – replace with a new one if not.

With pipe joints, check that the olive is securely fitted to the pipe, about 5mm from the end. If it is, smear some sealing compound around the olive before remaking the joint.

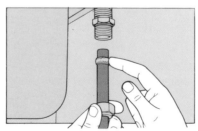

Leaks from pipe joints can occur even if the olive is securely in place. Smear sealing compound or wrap PTFE tape around the olive and then remake the joint.

Curing airlocks

An uneven, spluttering flow is probably due to an airlock. Correct this on a pillar tap by connecting a hose from a mains-fed tap to it. With spluttering from a kitchen hot tap for example, connect the hose from the cold tap to it and then turn both taps on fully.

For a mixer tap, remove the spout and block the opening with a clean towel. Press down on the towel and then get someone to turn on the hot tap followed by the cold tap. After a minute or two, turn off the cold tap followed by the hot tap.

Connecting a hose from the cold tap to the hot and turning both taps on fully should quickly force an airlock out of the hot supply pipe.

CHANGING BATHROOM TAPS

Changing bathroom taps puts an end to persistent faults once and for all, as well as giving the room a new lease of life. It also presents the ideal opportunity to uprate your taps to modern ceramic disc models, or to fit a bath shower mixer – the simplest form of shower.

There are of course many other tap options, including monobloc and three hole mixers, and remote control fittings (as found on corner baths). These are not covered here, since they can't normally be fitted as straight replacements to a conventional suite. However, if you're changing the suite as well, the principles are the same.

What the job involves

Theoretically, changing bathroom taps is much the same as changing kitchen taps, and uses many of the same bits and pieces (see below). The main difference is that bathroom suites tend to be a lot less robust than sinks, which means taking extra care – particularly when removing the old fittings. Where mixer taps are concerned, the layout of your plumbing may also affect the job's feasibility (see Problem Solver).

.... Shopping List ....

The choices available: ceramic disc pillar taps (top), two-hole bath mixer (centre) and two-hole thermostatic shower mixer (above).

Bathroom taps come in a huge range of styles. Many of the differences are purely cosmetic, but you have a fundamental choice between older-style *washered mechanisms* and modern *ceramic disc cartridges*. Ceramic disc taps are easier to operate and virtually maintenance-free, but tend to be more costly.

The standard sizes (measured by the inlet) are ½″ for basins, ¾″ for baths. If you have a tank-fed system, avoid Continental taps with smaller inlets; these are designed for mains pressure systems and may not allow sufficient flow.

Two-hole mixers for baths should have the standard spacing of 180mm (7″) between tails. Some models have adjustable tails.

Two-hole shower mixers are now available with thermostatic control, though on a low pressure system the flow rate may be poor.

There are restrictions on how and where mixers can be fitted, so check Problem Solver first.

YOU WANT	YOU NEED	YOU MAY NEED
New pillar taps	* The taps * Fibre washers * Adjustable wrenches * Tap tool, basin spanner or adjustable tap wrench * Penetrating oil	* Shank adaptors * Top-hat washers (pressed steel enamelled and plastic suites only) * Anti-rotational washers
Two-hole mixer (bath only)	* Tap unit * Fibre washers * Adjustable wrenches * Tap tool, basin spanner or adjustable tap wrench * Penetrating oil	* Shank adaptors * PTFE tape * Top-hat washers or bracing plate
Two-hole shower mixer (bath only)	* Tap unit * Shower head and hose * Wall fixing bracket * Adjustable wrenches * Tap tool, basin spanner or adjustable tap wrench * Penetrating oil	* Shank adaptors * PTFE tape * Top-hat washers or bracing plate * Non-return valve * Ceramic wall tiles

REMOVING THE OLD TAPS

Removing the old taps is usually the most difficult part of the job, and even plumbers approach it with trepidation. As well as the problem of access to the backnuts holding the tap tails, you are quite likely to find that the taps are stuck fast in old sealant.

Unlike a sink, you can't simply rely on brute force. China suites are especially vulnerable to cracking, but even enamelled steel and acrylic plastic baths can suffer damage if the taps are allowed to turn in their holes. The answer is to be well prepared before you start.

Gaining access

Where possible, unscrew and remove any boxing-in around a basin to give yourself as much room as possible. If the basin is set into a vanitory unit, it's worth taking the trouble to remove the unit doors and shelves.

Acrylic bath panels simply clip on. Otherwise, look for screws or 'push on/off' magnetic catches holding the panel. Part of the supporting framework may also need to be removed, so that there's enough room to reach under the bath.

Before starting in earnest, check that the tools you have available are capable of bearing firmly on the tap backnuts; if not, there's no point in going any further. The usual options are:
- A 'universal' tap tool.
- A basin ('Crowsfoot') spanner.
- An adjustable tap wrench.

If you can get the supply pipes out of the way, it may be that an ordinary box spanner (as used for car repairs) works best since this allows you to apply more torque (turning force). Otherwise, hire or borrow the relevant tool.

Preparing to start

If the tap tails are corroded or caked with grime and scale, clean them with steel wool or a wire brush. Then, in all cases, squirt penetrating oil around the backnuts and tail threads, and leave this to work its way along the threads for at least two hours.

Working from above, devise a way to stop the taps turning as you loosen the backnuts. Normally, a piece of wood bearing against the nearest wall is sufficient, but if you're working alone cut a notch in it so that it can be wedged firmly. Remember, the tap will turn in the same direction as the nuts – *clockwise* viewed from above.

Finally, pour some boiling water over the base of the taps to soften the old sealant. (On no account use direct heat, whatever the suite is made of.)

Trade tip

Get comfortable

❝ You'd be surprised how much easier it is to wrestle with old taps if you start from a comfortable working position: try various approaches and see which is easiest, using cushions as padding if necessary. You also need plenty of light, so rig up an inspection lamp on an extension lead. ❞

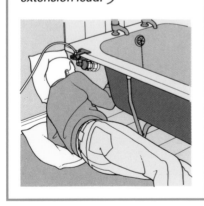

PREPARING THE TAPS

use batten to stop tap turning when undoing backnuts

soften old sealant with boiling water

check how to loosen backnuts

apply penetrating oil to backnuts and tail threads

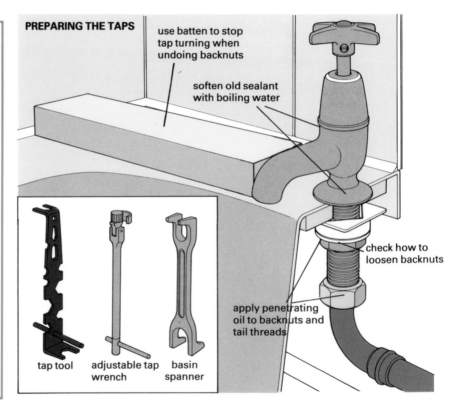

tap tool

adjustable tap wrench

basin spanner

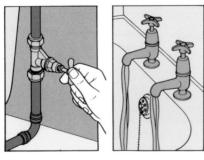

1 *Isolate the supplies to the taps (bathroom stopcocks are often hidden behind the bath panel). Open the taps to drain any water left in the pipes.*

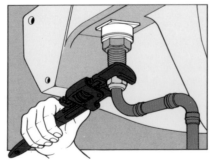

2 *Use an adjustable wrench to undo the tap connectors holding the supply pipes to the tap tails. Ease the pipes out of the way (but don't force them).*

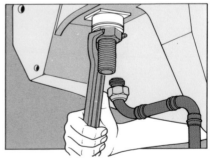

3 *From above, make sure the tap is supported to stop it from turning. From below, loosen the backnuts with the appropriate tool, then remove the tap.*

FITTING THE NEW TAPS

Pillar taps and mixers all fit in basically the same way, but there are certain restrictions on how and where mixers can be fitted (see Problem Solver overleaf). The first job is to test-fit the new taps to see how they match up to the existing supply pipes:

If the tails are too short, there may be enough free play in the pipes to make up the difference – but don't force them. If not, fit *tap shank adaptors* between the tails and the existing tap connectors.

If the new taps are plastic, you may be able to get away with using the existing brass connectors by winding a single turn of PTFE tape around the threads of the tails before connecting. Do not overtighten.

Or fit plastic tap adaptors (usually supplied) as shown on the right.

If the tap bodies are a loose fit in their holes, buy *anti-rotational washers* to stop them moving.

If the suite material is too thin to tighten the backnuts, fit *top-hat washers* to make up the thickness – you'll probably find they were fitted to the old taps.

For a bath mixer fitted to an acrylic bath, make up a *bracing plate* from plywood; cut it roughly to the size of the tap body and drill holes for the tails at 180mm (7″) centres.

Other points to watch

■ As when removing the old taps, take care not to let the new taps turn as you tighten the backnuts.

■ Do not overtighten the backnuts.

■ Convention has it that hot goes on the left and cold on the right. There may be a problem if the supply pipes are installed the other way and you are fitting a shower mixer (see Problem Solver).

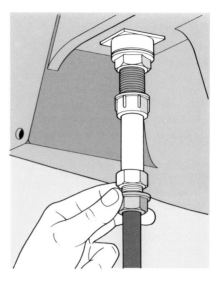

***Plastic taps** may require compression-jointed adaptors. Cut the supply pipes with a hacksaw at the appropriate points and file off the burrs before fitting.*

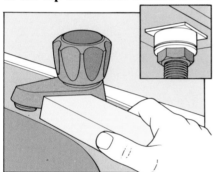

1 *Position the new tap and sealing gasket and support it against being turned. (Fit an anti-rotational washer if the tap is a loose fit in the hole.)*

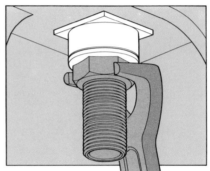

2 *Working from below, fit any washers supplied (or required) then screw on the backnut. Steadying the tap, tighten the backnut with the appropriate tool.*

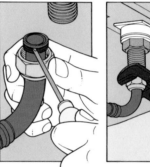

3 *Dig out the old washer in the tap connector with a bradawl and fit a new one. Screw the connector to the end of the tap tail and tighten with a wrench.*

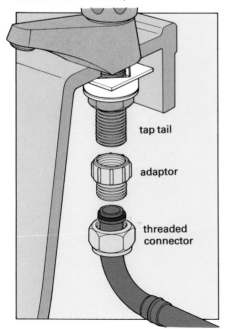

tap tail

adaptor

threaded connector

***Fit a shank adaptor** to bridge the gap between existing supply pipes and short tap tails. Screw the adaptor to the tail and tighten, then screw on the tap connector.*

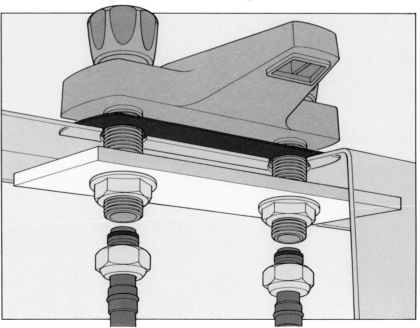

***Bath mixers** need a plywood bracing plate if fitted to an acrylic bath. Top-hat washers are nearly always required, but should already have been fitted to the old taps. The shower head hose simply screws to the outlet nozzle.*

47

Bath mixer restrictions

There are several restrictions on fitting bath mixer taps. Make sure you understand them before buying, since they could affect what sort of tap you choose.

For all types of mixer tap, check whether the model you plan to buy mixes the hot and cold supplies in the body of the tap or keeps them separate until they leave the spout.

If the tap is the 'mix in body' type, but the hot and cold supplies are fed via a cold storage tank and hot water cylinder, you have no problems. However, if the cold supply comes direct from the mains, the Water Byelaws insist that you fit a double check valve assembly directly below the inlet to the tap to guard against stored hot water being siphoned back into the mains.

On taps which keep the flow separate, if the supply is from the mains, check that the diverter valve is spring-loaded to guard against back-siphonage of waste bath water through the hose. If not, you must fit a double check valve.

For shower mixer taps there are some practical considerations.

If the supply is via a cold storage tank and hot water cylinder, the water outlets from the tank should be sufficiently high above the shower head to give a reasonable amount of pressure (the 'head' as it is known in the trade). About 1m (3′) is the minimum acceptable, otherwise you could find the diverter valve keeps switching back to the bath-filling position.

Another point to consider is the number of other taps branched off the same supply pipes. Theoretically, turning several taps on at the same time could alter the shower pressure (creating a risk of scalding unless the mixer is thermostatically controlled). In practice the risk is usually minimal and is worth taking. But if you do experience pressure drop problems, the only solution is to run new supply pipes to the tap directly from the cold storage tank and from the hot water cylinder vent pipe, close to the cylinder.

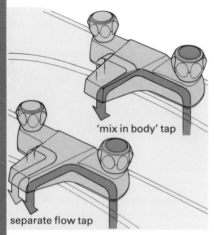

Check before buying whether or not the mixer tap keeps the hot and cold supplies separate.

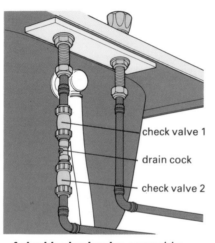

A double check valve assembly may be needed on a mixer tap fed directly from the mains supply.

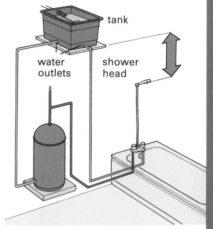

For adequate pressure the shower head should be at least 1m (3′) below the tank outlets.

Reversing pipes

If you're fitting a conventional mixer and the pipes are the wrong way round (ie with cold on the left), you should be able to solve the problem by swapping the coloured indicators on (or in) the handles.

However, on thermostatic mixers you have to reverse the pipes so that the controls aren't the wrong way round. The easiest way to do this is by fitting a pair of *bendable connectors* with tap connector fittings at one end and compression, soldered or push-fit joints on the other. Shape the connectors to make the cross-over **before** you cut the supply pipes though, otherwise you are likely to find they don't fit.

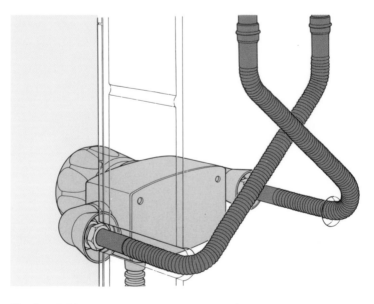

Use bendable connectors to reverse supply pipes connected the wrong way round if you are fitting a thermostatically controlled shower.

PLUMBING IN A WASHING MACHINE

Plumbing in a washing machine for fully automatic operation is a job where it pays to have a go yourself. Often, modern connection gadgets make it possible to do without plumbing skills altogether. And even where the installation isn't quite so easy, you can save money by doing some of the work yourself, then calling in a plumber for the tricky parts.

Siting the machine

The job falls neatly into two stages: providing a water supply, and arranging drainage.

As a rule, the nearer the washing machine is to hot and cold pipes and to a drainage outlet, the easier the installation. For many people, this means siting the machine in the kitchen, near the sink. But cloakrooms and downstairs utility rooms shouldn't be ruled out, since they, too, often have the necessary plumbing facilities – plus the advantage of more space.

Bathrooms are more of a problem. The regulations on using electrical appliances here are so restrictive that in most cases it simply isn't practical to install a washing machine. In a very large bathroom it may just be possible, but seek expert advice before proceeding.

Making connections

When you've decided on a location, run through the connection options overleaf and see which suit it best. You should also read through the installation details supplied with the washing machine and make a note of any special recommendations.

Supply With some machines, you have a choice of connecting to both hot and cold supplies, or to cold only (so saving on hot water). The connections are the same for both.

Drainage Most machines pump out the waste water, allowing you to connect the drain hose to the nearest waste pipe via a special trap or a screw-in connector. But a few still rely on siphonage to remove the waste, and must be connected via a vertical *standpipe*.

Some makers also advise standpipe installation as a safeguard against blockages caused by fluff. In this case, connection by any other method may invalidate the warranty.

Where a washing machine is within easy reach of water supply pipes and a drainage outlet, it can be plumbed in simply using DIY connectors.

.... Shopping List ....

Washing machine plumb-in kits normally give you all the parts needed for Supply or Waste Options 1 overleaf. For other types of supply connection you may need:

Washing machine stoptaps These are sold with push-fit or compression connections for the supply pipes, and threaded connections for the machine supply hoses.

15mm supply pipe and fittings These can be plastic push-fit or copper with compression joints. Work out the length and direction of the pipe runs beforehand: you'll need tee fittings for joining to the existing pipes, plus 90° elbows for making bends. Buy pipe clips, wallplugs and screws if the runs are longer than 1m (3').

For other types of waste connection you may need:

Washing machine trap This replaces an existing plastic sink trap and has a mixture of screw-on and adjustable push-fit parts, enabling alignment with the existing pipes. There is normally a push-on fitting for the machine outlet hose.

Standpipe These are sold in kit form, complete with trap. Buy 38mm (1½″) plastic pipe plus wall clips to make up a new waste run, or a *swept tee* fitting for connection to an existing waste pipe. Choose from push-fit or solvent-weld (glued) joints. See Problem Solver for other types of waste connection.

Tools (depending on connection method): junior hacksaw, adjustable spanner, electric drill.

Self-cutting connectors (below) for the supply and waste pipes get round the need for traditional plumbing skills.

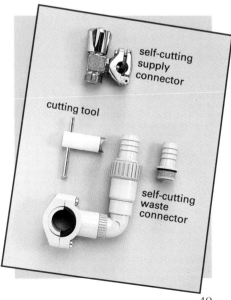

self-cutting supply connector

cutting tool

self-cutting waste connector

SUPPLY OPTIONS

1: SELF-CUTTING CONNECTORS

The simplest way of joining to the existing hot and cold pipes is to use self-cutting connectors. As long as the taps on the fittings are kept closed, you don't even have to turn off the water.

Each connector has a clamp which you fit around the supply pipe, and a stoptap which then screws into the clamp. The stoptap inlet contains a circular cutter that automatically breaks through the pipe wall, plus a washer to guarantee a watertight join.

Various makes work slightly differently, but two main types of stoptap are available. Within reach of the washing machine hoses, choose taps with threaded outlets that allow you to attach the hoses directly. For connections some way from the machine, opt for taps with compression fittings on the outlets so you can run branch pipes as in Supply Option 2, and then fit hose connectors to the pipe ends.

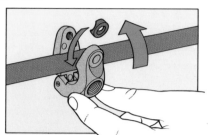

1 Decide where to site the stoptap, then offer up the clamp to the pipe. Some types fix to the wall, in which case drill and plug, then screw in place.

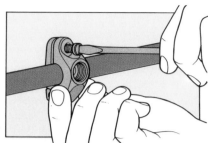

2 Screw the clamp body together over the pipe. Some are in two parts while others are hinged. The clamp body has a screw thread inside to accept the tap body.

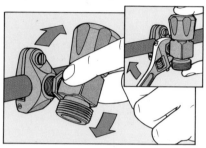

3 Screw the tap body into the clamp until it's hand-tight. Some types need an extra quarter of a turn with a spanner. Adjust the tap body so it is vertical.

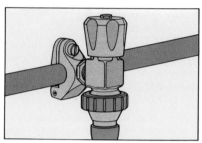

4 The tap shown is threaded for direct hose connection. With the sealing washer inside the plastic hose connector, screw it on and tighten with a spanner.

2: BRANCH PIPES WITH TEES

The conventional way of supplying a washing machine is to turn the water off and insert tee fittings in the supply pipes. From here, you run branch pipes to a point near the machine and fit compression-jointed stoptaps with threaded outlets to accept the machine hoses. See overleaf for how to make connections in copper pipes.

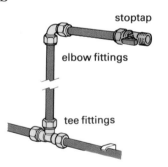

stoptap

elbow fittings

tee fittings

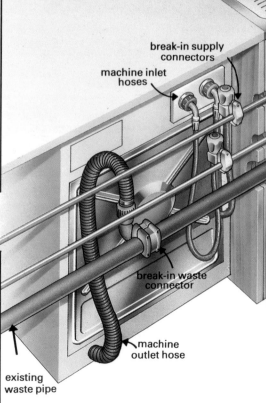

break-in supply connectors

machine inlet hoses

break-in waste connector

existing waste pipe

machine outlet hose

3: STOPTAP TEE FITTINGS

This is a variation of Option 2, used where the connections to the supply pipes can be made close to the machine, but where you aren't allowed to use self-cutting connectors.

Instead, you cut the supply and fit compression jointed tee fittings with built-in stoptaps. As with Option 1, these allow the hoses to be attached direct.

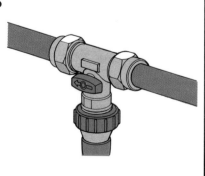

Above: A typical installation near the kitchen sink, using self-cutting connectors to break into the supply and waste pipes.

WASTE OPTIONS

1: DIRECT CONNECTION

If there is a sink waste pipe running behind or along the side of the machine (and providing the machine is suitable), connect the outlet hose directly to it using a self-cutting connector similar to the one used in Supply Option 1. Such connectors are designed to fit standard 38mm (1½″) pipe.

You don't need any special tools: the connector has its own cutting tool which is removed from the saddle clamp once the hole has been cut, ready for the hose connector assembly to be screwed to the clamp body.

 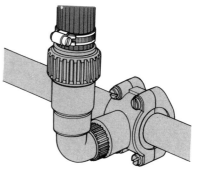

1 Fit the adjustable clamp (complete with internal seal) round the waste pipe and screw in the cutter to make the hole. Remove the cutter.

2 Attach the hose connector and non-return valve to the clamp, with or without the elbow supplied, depending on the angle. Then fit the machine outlet hose.

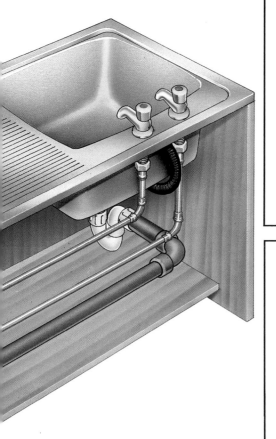

2: REPLACE SINK TRAP

Near the kitchen sink, it may be easier to replace the sink trap with one incorporating a washing machine hose outlet.

Unscrew the old trap, using a damp cloth to grip the locking rings. Assemble the new trap according to the instructions, then screw to the sink outlet and waste pipe, letting the trap's push-fit joints take up any adjustment. Finally, fit the drain hose to the outlet on the side of the trap.

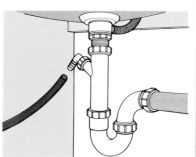

Washing machine traps have an outlet for the machine's drain hose. They are a simple replacement for the whole of an existing plastic sink trap.

3: FIT STANDPIPE

A standpipe prevents siphonage of the waste during washing by incorporating an air break.

The standpipe itself should be about 600mm (24″) high (check the machine instructions), and must have a trap fitted below it. If there is an existing waste pipe running near the machine at floor level, connect the standpipe as shown. See Problem Solver if you have to run a new waste pipe.

1 Mark the position of the swept tee fitting on the waste pipe, allowing for the amount taken up by the joints. Cut the pipe with a junior hacksaw.

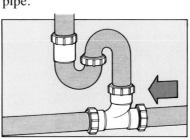 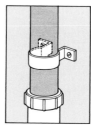 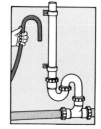

2 Fit the tee fitting with the swept part angled in the direction of the flow. Follow by adding the two parts of the trap and the standpipe.

3 Secure the assembly to the wall using 38mm (1½″) pipe clips. Finally, simply slip the washing machine outlet hose into the top of the standpipe.

Local bye-laws
Some water authorities only permit certain types of connection, and others forbid taking the cold supply direct from the rising main. Phone the authority's engineer's department and check what rules apply in your area before buying any parts.

TRADITIONAL CONNECTIONS

Breaking into the hot and cold supplies (and if necessary, running branch pipes) isn't too difficult so long as you can turn off the water. The method shown uses 15mm copper pipe with compression joints.

If you take the cold supply from the rising main, don't forget to turn off the water at the main stopcock. If the supply is fed from a storage tank, check the machine's instructions – you may need to remove the flow inhibitor fitted on the inlet hose. In all cases, open the nearest taps to drain down the pipes before cutting into them.

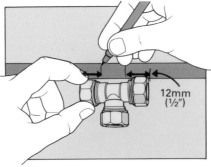
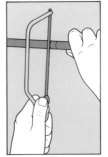
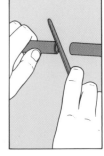

1 *To fit a tee, offer up the fitting and mark how much needs to be cut out of the supply pipe. Subtract 12mm (½") each side to allow for the joints.*

2 *Cut the pipe using a junior hacksaw. Use an old knife or nailfile to smooth off the ends, then slip on the capnuts and sealing rings (olives).*

Trade tip

Cutting tips

❝ If you find it difficult to get at a pipe with your saw, try removing the blade and refitting it the other way round – from behind the pipe.

To help cut the ends square, wrap pieces of tape around where you want to cut and use these as a guide. ❞

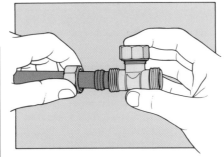
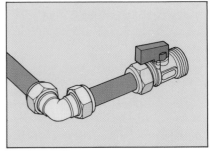

3 *Slip the tee over one pipe end, then slot in the other pipe end. Slide the olives up to the tee, wrap on some PTFE tape, then tighten the capnuts.*

4 *Assemble branch pipes in the same way, using compression elbow fittings where you need to turn corners. Fit washing machine stoptaps at the end of the runs.*

▌PROBLEM SOLVER▐

Arranging drainage

When problems do arise with washing machines, it's usually either because there is no convenient trap or waste pipe to break into, or because you need to fit a standpipe and the existing waste pipe is too high. The diagrams show two possible solutions.

One is to run a new length of waste pipe out through the house wall to a nearby gully. For this, you'll need a hammer drill and heavy duty masonry bit long enough to pierce the brickwork.

The other is to connect a new run of waste pipe to a nearby plastic soil pipe using a fitting called a *strap-on boss connector*. If you're lucky, the soil pipe will be inside the house (though it may be hidden behind vertical boxing). If the soil pipe is outside, you'll have to run the pipe through the wall. Old cast-iron soil pipes are not suitable for connection in this way.

Arrange for the new waste pipe to slope fractionally so that the water drains correctly. (The exact slope is not critical.)

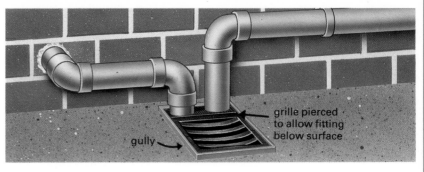

At a gully, run the pipe down below the surface of the grille (old open type), or connect into the spare inlet hole (modern closed type).

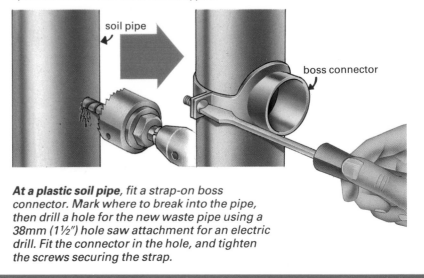

At a plastic soil pipe, fit a strap-on boss connector. Mark where to break into the pipe, then drill a hole for the new waste pipe using a 38mm (1½") hole saw attachment for an electric drill. Fit the connector in the hole, and tighten the screws securing the strap.

PLUMBING IN A DISHWASHER

Plumbing in a dishwasher is no more difficult than plumbing in a washing machine – and in many cases it's easier. Normally there are less restrictions on how and where you can make the connections. And the dishwasher's natural location – beside the kitchen sink – means that there are water and drainage supplies conveniently close to hand.

Unlike washing machines, however, most dishwasher ranges include models for building into an existing run of kitchen units. These are designed to fit a standard 600mm (2′) wide base unit, and can be fitted either with a laminate 'decor' panel or a false door front to match the kitchen system. Most also have removable plinths and adjustable feet, for easy fitting under a worktop.

If building-in is an important consideration, make sure your chosen model is designed with this in mind. Check too, that the maker of the kitchen units offers laminate panels or door fronts as accessories.

A dishwasher can be built into an existing run of kitchen units.

....Shopping List....

Before you buy any parts, read through the maker's installation instructions: these are largely the same from model to model, but there may be specific recommendations that have to be followed in order to validate the guarantee.

Water supply Most dishwashers are cold-fill only (or are recommended for such), so you can take the supply from the rising main feeding the sink cold tap.

The easiest method is to fit a washing machine *self-cutting connector* incorporating a stoptap tee and a standard ¾″ BSP thread for the dishwasher supply hose. Make sure the connector you buy carries water authority approval.

Drainage outlet Break into the sink waste pipe using a 38mm (1½″) self-cutting connector, or replace the existing sink trap with a *washing machine trap* incorporating a hose connection. (Some makers recommend installing a washing

machine standpipe, but this isn't strictly necessary if you take care how you fit the dishwasher drain hose – see overleaf. For other supply and drainage problems, see pages 49-52.

If the dishwasher is to be built in, the instructions will give details of what size laminate decor panel or door front to order. Decor panels are clipped to the door of the machine using the trim pieces supplied. False doors screw to

brackets or lugs on the front of the machine. Buy a 600mm (24″) length of new plinth panel to match the units if you can't adapt the old one to fit.

Tools checklist: Screwdriver, adjustable spanner, electric drill and bits, panel saw, tape measure.

A typical connection set-up (below), showing the inlet hose supplied via a self-cutting connector and the outlet hose linked to a washing machine trap.

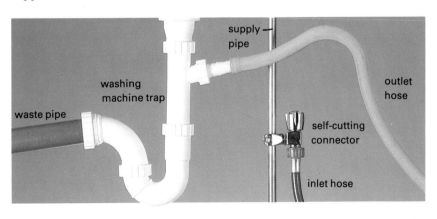

ARRANGING THE WATER SUPPLY

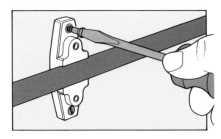 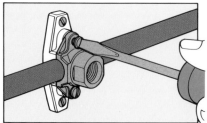 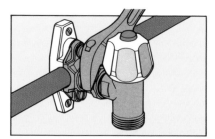

1 *Choose an accessible site for the self-cutting connector within easy reach of the dishwasher hose. For a wall-mounted type, drill and plug holes and screw in place.*

2 *Fit the clamp over the pipe – some types are hinged, others are in two parts – not forgetting the internal seal if supplied. Screw the two parts of the connector tightly together.*

3 *Screw in the stoptap to pierce the pipe wall (some types need an extra turn with a spanner), and adjust it to sit vertically. Fit the rubber seal in the supply hose and screw to the outlet.*

ARRANGING DRAINAGE

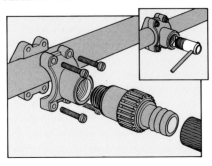 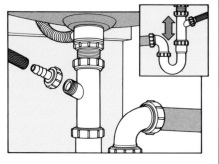

Option 1: fit a self-cutting connector to the existing waste pipe. Screw in the cutter, then attach the hose connector and non-return valve, followed by the machine outlet hose.

Option 2: fit a washing machine trap in place of the sink trap. Most types have sliding seal joints and need no adjustment, otherwise trim the parts to fit with a hacksaw.

Trade tip

Avoiding siphonage

❝ If there isn't a non-return valve on the drainage outlet, avoid back-siphonage by curving the machine's outlet hose over the trap or waste pipe connector as shown. If necessary, fix up a bracket using a cup hook and a piece of wire. ❞

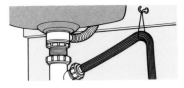

BUILDING IN

Where there is a convenient 600mm (2') wide unit: simply remove it and slot the dishwasher into the vacant space. (In a new kitchen, you can allow for this at the planning stage.) Where the units are all 500mm (20") or 1m (3'3") wide, remove a metre's worth and custom-build a unit to fit the 400mm (16") gap that's left.

To remove a unit:

■ Unclip or unscrew the plinth (you may be able to re-use it).
■ Remove any doors or drawers, plus their hinges and runners.
■ Remove the drawers in the units on either side and undo the cabinet connecting screws linking them.
■ Remove any screws joining the unit to the worktop.
■ Slacken the adjustable feet (if fitted) and slide out the unit.

Fitting the machine

■ Prepare the machine following the instructions. This may involve unscrewing the plinth, the false worktop and the door assembly.
■ Slide the machine into position and level using the adjustable feet. This is likely to be the most convenient time to make the plumbing connections. You may have to cut slots or drill holes for the pipework in the adjacent units.
■ Screw the false door to the machine (you may need to supply fixing screws), or fit the decor panel using the trim strips supplied.
■ Refit the old plinth, or a new section. You may have to cut a piece out of the plinth to clear the door. Do this with a jig saw, drilling holes in the corners so the blade can cut the 'blind' side.

A typical built-in set-up (left): the false door screws to spring-loaded brackets and closes with the machine door.
Laminate decor panels (inset) clip directly to the machine door using the trim strips supplied.

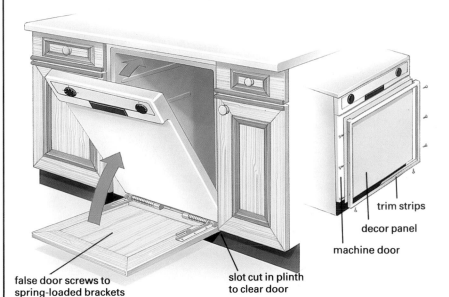

false door screws to spring-loaded brackets

slot cut in plinth to clear door

trim strips

decor panel

machine door

PLUMBING IN AN ELECTRIC SHOWER

Electrically heated 'instantaneous' showers have become increasingly popular in recent years, and are certainly worth considering if you are thinking of installing new shower facilities. This section describes how to fit the shower and run the water supply.

Pros and cons

An electric shower heats mains-pressure cold water as it flows through the body of the unit to give a constant and virtually limitless flow at the shower head. This is obviously an advantage from an economy point of view, since the water is only heated when required, and no heat is wasted in long pipe runs or storage cylinders.

Complete independence from the hot water system also gives plenty of flexibility over positioning – with only a single 15mm pipe from the rising main to connect, electric showers are by far the easiest to plumb in. Unfortunately this advantage is offset to some extent by the need for an independent electricity supply from the consumer unit. All in all, there are unlikely to be major savings in time and materials over other types.

The other drawback to an electric shower is that it may not be as invigorating – or as hot – as you expect. The flow of water through the head depends on how quickly it can be heated (see below), but even the most powerful models don't compare too favourably with a properly installed conventional shower. Also, the need to provide the head with a fine spray to make the most of the flow means that a lot of heat can get lost to the air unless the room itself is kept warm.

An electric shower – the instant way to freshen up.

Trade tip
Hard water facts

❝ In hard water areas, scale build-up can be a severe problem for electric showers. The way round it is to fit a water softener in the supply branch – either an electromagnetic type, or a dosing unit designed for instantaneous heaters. Details are given in Problem Solver.

Note, however, that some electronic showers can't be used with a mains-fitted regenerative salt water softener; check with the supplier before buying. ❞

....Shopping List....

Electrically heated showers were among the first appliances to take advantage of the microchip, with the result that nearly all models are *electronic* – many with automatic temperature control.

The main buying consideration is size – in other words, the power of the heater. The smallest showers are rated at 6kW, but 7kW is the practical minimum for a reasonable flow. 8.4kW showers give 20% more flow than 7kW models, but even these only deliver a moderately powerful spray when the incoming water is coldest.

Electric showers are widely available from DIY superstores and plumbers merchants, and normally come complete with an adjustable shower head and bracket. For plumbing you need:
15mm pipe – choose from copper, plastic or stainless steel.
Matching fittings – push fit, compression or soldered – and pipe clips.
A stopcock to isolate the supply.
Pipe insulation, where the pipe runs through the roof space.
Screws and wallplugs etc for fixing the shower unit. You may also need materials for hiding the pipe/cable and making good – see overleaf and Problem Solver.

The Water Byelaws require that shower heads capable of being dangled in a bath or shower tray must have a *check valve* fitted between the head and the hose. This is available as an optional extra with most showers, but may only be obtainable direct from the makers.
Tools checklist: Wrenches, screwdrivers, electric drill and bits, tools for making good and redecorating.

PLANNING THE INSTALLATION

The easiest place to position a shower is on the end wall over the bath, where drainage is already taken care of and there is probably some form of splash-resistant surface. The drawback is that this doesn't provide a separate shower facility – often the main reason for having a shower in the first place.

If you do choose the bath, make sure the surfaces around the shower are suitable – either tiles with waterproof grout, or eggshell paint. You may need to extend a tiled splashback to suit, in which case do so after fitting the shower so that the pipe and cable can be buried in the wall. You should also decide what other splash protections you need – either a curtain or splash panels – and position the shower unit accordingly.

A separate shower cubicle can go in the bathroom, a bedroom, a downstairs cloakroom – or even under the stairs. The main restriction is whether or not you can run a 38mm (1½") waste pipe from here to a nearby stack or gully. Also, showers mustn't be fitted within 2.5m (8'2½") of a power socket or conventional light switch.

Check the points shown below before finalizing what you need, then make a list. In particular, decide how you are going to hide the pipe and cable – see Problem Solver if the shower area is tiled, and you need to surface mount them.

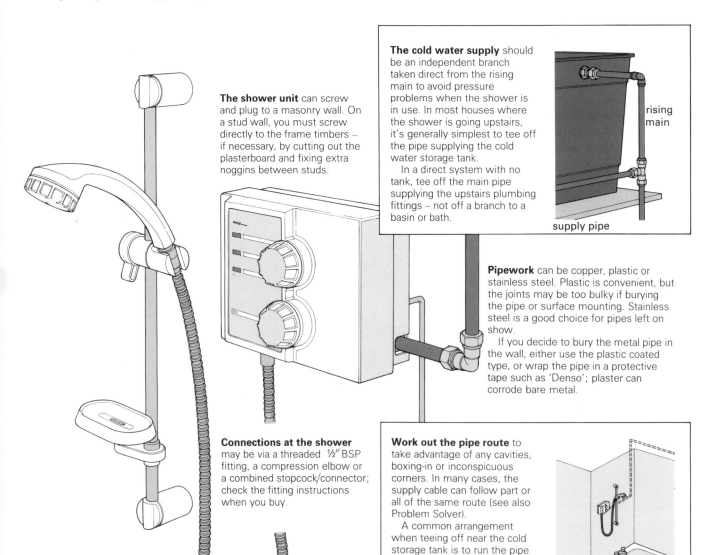

The shower unit can screw and plug to a masonry wall. On a stud wall, you must screw directly to the frame timbers – if necessary, by cutting out the plasterboard and fixing extra noggins between studs.

The cold water supply should be an independent branch taken direct from the rising main to avoid pressure problems when the shower is in use. In most houses where the shower is going upstairs, it's generally simplest to tee off the pipe supplying the cold water storage tank.

In a direct system with no tank, tee off the main pipe supplying the upstairs plumbing fittings – not off a branch to a basin or bath.

rising main

supply pipe

Pipework can be copper, plastic or stainless steel. Plastic is convenient, but the joints may be too bulky if burying the pipe or surface mounting. Stainless steel is a good choice for pipes left on show.

If you decide to bury the metal pipe in the wall, either use the plastic coated type, or wrap the pipe in a protective tape such as 'Denso'; plaster can corrode bare metal.

Connections at the shower may be via a threaded ½"BSP fitting, a compression elbow or a combined stopcock/connector; check the fitting instructions when you buy.

Work out the pipe route to take advantage of any cavities, boxing-in or inconspicuous corners. In many cases, the supply cable can follow part or all of the same route (see also Problem Solver).

A common arrangement when teeing off near the cold storage tank is to run the pipe through the floor, down the corner, and across the wall to the shower.

Trade tip

Check the seals
❝When fitting a shower over the bath, don't forget to check the condition of the sealant between the bath and the wall – many people overlook this, only to find that the ceiling comes crashing down a few months later because the water has seeped down behind the bath and gathered in the ceiling cavity. ❞

The electricity supply must be via a separate cable wired to its own fuseway in the consumer unit; the size of cable and the fuse rating of the circuit are determined by the total length of the run and by the power output of the shower.

A suitable double pole isolating switch must be fitted in the supply cable. Normally, it's best to use a 45 amp pull cord ceiling shower switch.

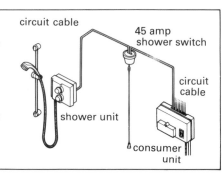

circuit cable

45 amp shower switch

circuit cable

shower unit

consumer unit

FITTING THE SHOWER

Plumbing in the shower is straight-forward, but if you work in a methodical order it will save you having to do things twice.

■ Establish the position of the shower unit and shower head bracket, then mark the pipe and cable runs.

■ If the pipe and/or cable are being buried in the wall, cut channels (chases) in the plaster.

■ Run the pipe and cable to where you plan to connect to the unit.

■ Plaster over the pipe and cable.

■ Fit the shower tray (where appropriate).

■ Tile and grout the wall (where appropriate), then fit the shower.

■ Connect the supply pipe to the rising main.

■ Connect the supply pipe to the shower, then make the electrical connections.

■ Fit any shower cubicle/surround.

Fitting tips

■ Showers come fully assembled, so start by checking the fitting instructions, then remove the knobs and casing screws and put them back in the box for safe keeping.

■ On a tiled wall, try to position the backing box to coincide with the grout lines.

■ It's advisable – and on some models essential – to position the shower unit so that it is outside the line of the spray. There may be specific advice in the instructions.

■ Check – if necessary with a metal detector – that there are no buried pipes or cables where you plan to screw the shower to the wall.

The instructions here take you as far as connecting the pipework, though in most cases you will be running the electric cable at the same time. Leave the cover off until the electrical connection is made.

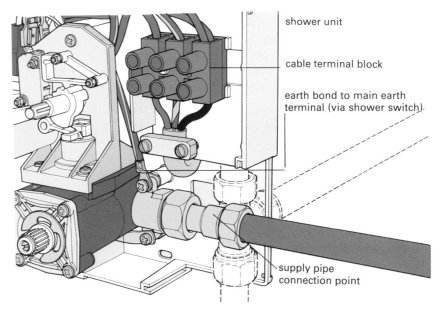

shower unit

cable terminal block

earth bond to main earth terminal (via shower switch)

supply pipe connection point

Some showers have a choice of entry ports for the pipe and cable. These allow top, bottom, or sideways entry – or even through the back for total concealment.

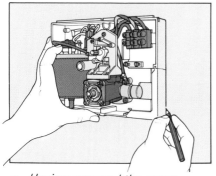

1 *Having removed the cover, offer up the unit and draw around it. Mark the fixing holes, followed by the pipe and cable entry points.*

2 *Put the shower unit safely to one side. Cut chases if burying the pipe/cable, or fit the mini-trunking (see overleaf) if surface mounting.*

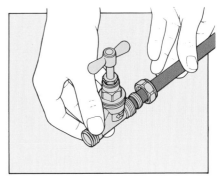

3 *Run the pipe between the shower and the connection point. Fit a stopcock somewhere accessible, making sure the flow arrow points towards the shower.*

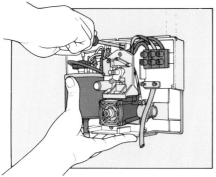

4 *Screw and plug the wall, and fit the shower unit. Before connecting the supply at the shower end, flush the pipework by opening the stopcock momentarily.*

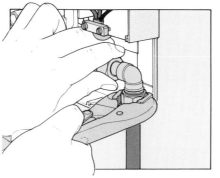

5 *Connect the supply pipe and tighten with an adjustable spanner or wrench, supporting the internal connections as you do so, to avoid straining them.*

Trade tip

Clip it tight

❝ Make sure the supply pipe is properly clipped or otherwise held along its run. If not, there is a real risk of water hammer whenever the solenoid valve in the shower stops the flow. ❞

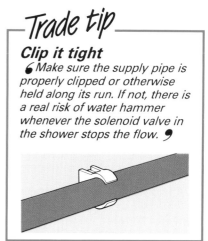

FITTING THE SPRAY HEAD

The shower head should be fixed to the wall so it is central to the shower tray or bath. With a sliding rail fitting, this means that the rail must be slightly off centre. The rail fixing positions are normally 600mm (2′) apart, which on a tiled wall usually means you can drill through the joints rather than the tiles themselves.

The height of the rail depends on who will be using the shower. Allowing 2m (6′6″) with the head at the top of the rail allows it to be lowered to 1.4m (4′7″), which suits most people.

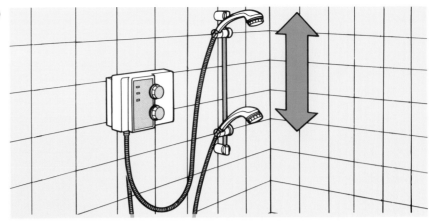

The shower head will probably be on a sliding bracket which should suit the tallest and shortest users.

PROBLEM SOLVER

Surface mounting pipes and cables

Pipe and cables running across the surface of the wall are an eyesore, but often the alternative – burying them beneath the surface – means unacceptable disruption to decorations. The simple answer is to use white plastic mini-trunking (eg 'Hideapipe') wide enough in section to take the pipe and cable side by side.

The trunking can be screwed to the wall, or stuck with impact adhesive if the length is fairly short; often a combination of the two methods is the best solution.

Corner and tee fittings are available for most makes, but try to avoid bends by finding the most direct route.

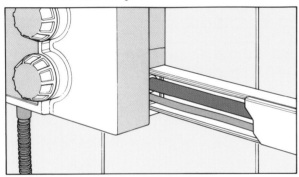

Fit mini-trunking backing sections before you run the pipe and cable. Lay them inside, then cut the cover sections and clip in place over the top.

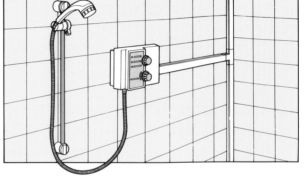

Where the pipe and cable come from opposite directions, run the trunking from floor to ceiling and take a short branch from here to the shower.

Dealing with scale

In severe hard water areas, a shower head may need descaling every fortnight. This means dismantling and scraping it down, or soaking it in scale remover – both tedious tasks.

Another, better way of tackling the problem is to fit a water softener/conditioner. Two types come as small compact units which are easily plumbed into the supply pipe:
Electro-magnetic conditioners work by changing the magnetic attraction of mineral particles in the water so that they stay there, instead of forming scale. **Chemical dosing** softeners work by releasing carefully measured doses of non-toxic chemicals into the water to soften it.

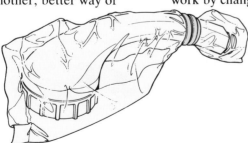

A way to descale the head is to tie a polythene bag filled with citric acid (available from home brewing stores) around it and leave to soak overnight.

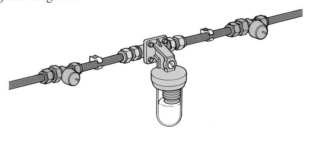

A better approach is to fit a water softener in the branch supply pipe. This is easily done using either push fit or compression fittings.

INSTALLING A VANITY UNIT

A vanity (or vanitory) unit is the rather quaint term used to describe a basin which is set into a floor-standing cupboard or cabinet rather than supported on a pedestal or brackets. Installing one from scratch in a bedroom or cloakroom is the perfect way to provide extra washing facilities and help relieve morning crushes in the family bathroom. But equally, there's no reason why a vanity unit can't go in the bathroom itself to provide valuable put-down space and handy storage for odds and ends.

Types of vanity unit

There are basically three ways to acquire a vanity unit:

■ Matched basins and units are now a feature of most bathroom suite ranges, and are often on display in bathroom showrooms and DIY superstores.

This is the safest option, since you can be sure that everything will fit together, but it may not provide the right look or combination of features. And if you are fitting into an

Vanity units provide plenty of storage space – and with a semi-countertop basin like this they don't need to take up much room.

awkward space, they may simply not be the right size. Standard units are commonly 820mm (32″) high, 600, 760, 1100 or 1200mm (24, 30, 44 or 48″) wide and 425–535mm (16–21″) deep.

■ Buying the unit and basin separately is slightly riskier and may involve making one or two extra modifications. However, it gives you a lot more choice.

☞ Adapting an existing piece of modular or free-standing furniture is potentially the trickiest option, but offers more scope for fitting an awkward space or creating something a little out of the ordinary. For example, you can set a basin in an antique or reproduction Victorian pine washstand to combine modern facilities with period furnishings. Equally, you can construct your own custom-made cupboard and give it the ideal dimensions and features.

THE BASIC OPTIONS

Buy a matched basin/unit

Buy the basin and unit separately

Adapt an existing piece of furniture

CHOOSING AND PLANNING A UNIT

If you are re-equipping the bathroom, think of the vanity unit in terms of the overall design. You may, for example, want to build it into a complete boxed-in run – perhaps incorporating the WC – or into some other kind of fitted furniture. The unit will also form a key part of your storage arrangements, so consider what you might want to put in it – or on it.

If the vanity unit is going elsewhere, the following points are worth bearing in mind.
■ Bedroom basins tend to accumulate lots of odds and ends, so putdown space and shelves for toiletries are useful features.
■ Basins used for hair washing, clothes washing or baby bathing need to be free of obstructions. Conventional pillar taps are often more practical in this respect than the latest monobloc mixers.
■ An unobtrusive location may be hard to come by. Alcoves and recesses are ideal, but if there aren't any you may be able to create one with fitted cupboards or modular built-in furniture.
■ Allow for an 'activity' area in front of the unit of at least 700×700mm (28×28″). Where space is tight, a semi-countertop basin will leave room for access to a shallow unit below.
■ Make sure there are no power

sockets or lighting plateswitches (except a bathroom shaver supply unit) within 2m (6′ 6″) of the unit. If there are, you should move them: you may be able to change a light switch for the pull-cord type.
■ Wherever the basin goes, the surrounding surfaces will need splash protection in the form of tiles or wallboards.

A fully-fitted bathroom can be designed so that it incorporates a vanity basin unit in a complete run of cupboards.

In the end, where you put the unit may rest on how easy it is to plumb in (see overleaf). Make sure you get the plumbing arrangements worked out before going ahead with the job.

BASIN AND TAP OPTIONS

Vanity basins can be:
Inset so that they fit through a hole in the countertop with a sealing lip.
Lay-on, in which the basin and countertop are a single unit which fits on top of the base.
Semi-countertop so that the back half of the basin is set into a narrow unit or shelf leaving the front half protruding.

Cheaper basins of enamelled steel or acrylic are nearly all the inset type, while as you move up-market, hardwearing porcelain and moulded resin join the list of options. Lay-on basins may be porcelain, moulded resin or the synthetic marble-like material Corian, but tend to be appreciably more expensive. Semi-countertop

basins are all porcelain, and also more costly than inset types.

Your choice of basin may well be influenced by what sort of taps you want. The cheapest have *two holes* for conventional pillar taps, while more up-market basin ranges offer *single holes* for monobloc mixers and *three holes* for mixers with separate controls and spout.

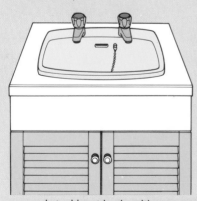

pressed steel inset basin with separate taps and combined overflow/waste

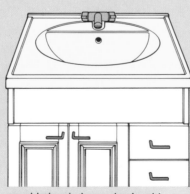

moulded resin lay-on basin with monobloc mixer

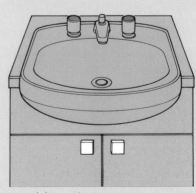

porcelain semi-countertop basin with three-hole mixer and pop-up waste

UNIT OPTIONS

Purpose-made units for vanity basins range from simple bases containing a pair of cupboards to double units for paired basins and elaborate floor-to-ceiling models incorporating wall cupboards or shelves, lights and mirrors. Most use some form of veneered chipboard construction and come flat-packed for self-assembly like kitchen units. However, you can also buy ready-made units and reproduction Victorian designs in solid mahogany or pine.

Units for inset and semi-countertop basins generally come with a solid top, leaving you to make the cut-out for the basin itself. Optional features may include interior shelves, a built-in mirror, and a matching or built-in medicine cabinet.

As with all self-assembly furniture, try to inspect a ready-assembled example before you buy. In particular, note the constructional quality of the doors and drawers, and avoid units where the veneer is thin or obviously chipping. It's also worth having a look at the assembly instructions if you can.

Adapting units

If you are looking for a unit or piece of furniture to adapt to take a vanity basin, the main things to watch are that it doesn't have a centre rail which could obstruct the basin cut-out, and that there is enough space *inside the frame* to accommodate the basin's maximum width. Drawers present less of a problem, since you can remove the insides and fix the front permanently in position.

Modular units can be put together in different ways to provide a basin plus all the facilities you need.

Double basin units are both practical and luxurious.

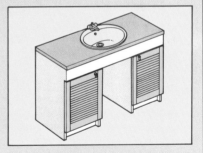

Dressing table units must have enough depth to fit the basin.

....Shopping List....

Complete vanity units should include all the basin fittings, joint fittings and fixing brackets, but it's as well to check – they are usually packed separately and may have been overlooked by the supplier. Ask about a cutting template for the top, too.

For a separate basin, make sure you have *taps, a waste outlet or pop-up waste mechanism, plumber's putty* for bedding the fittings, and *silicone sealant* for

sealing around the rim. See page 64 for more details.

Self-assembly units should include all the parts but the wall fixing screws; 50mm (2″) No. 10 woodscrews (and matching plugs) should do.

Plumbing requirements can only be estimated once you have planned the pipe routes (see overleaf). For supplies, don't forget *joint fittings, stopvalves, flexible tap connectors* and *pipe clips.* You may also need

slip couplings for teeing into existing pipes. For the waste, you need *suitable pipe and fittings* and a *bottle trap,* plus fittings to connect to the existing drains.

Tools checklist: Spanners and wrenches, screwdrivers, electric drill and bits, jigsaw, tape measure, hacksaw, file.

You may also need masonry tools for making holes in walls and lifting floorboards, and carpentry tools for adapting a unit to fit.

ARRANGING THE PLUMBING

Arranging the plumbing for a vanity unit can involve considerable disruption so it's as well to get it out of the way and make good before the unit is installed.

It's usually easier to lay on suitable hot and cold supplies before you do anything else. Run them as far as the proposed site of the unit, then fit stopvalves so that you can restore the household supply.

Running the waste pipe may be better left until the unit is installed so that you can ensure the correct fall. But as the proximity of the drains is likely to have a major influence on where you position the unit, it's as well to think about it at the earliest possible stage.

Technically, you need permission from the local Building Control Office to install a new drain run. In practice you can probably get away with describing what you plan to do over the phone, or submitting a sketch plan – but be sure to check.

Plumbing in a vanity unit in a bathroom should be no more difficult than any other type of basin.

Hot and cold supplies can be run in 15mm pipe as far as the unit from the nearest suitable pipes, leaving the final connections to be made using flexible tap connectors.

Drainage can be via a bottle trap and 32mm (1¼″) plastic waste pipe so long as the run is no longer than 1.7m (6′ 6″); if it is, switch to the 40mm (1½″) size. The pipe must have a slight fall, and you should avoid bends if possible. Fit *access tees* at bends which can't be unblocked.

The waste can run into a hopper head, or to a single plastic stack via a *connection boss*.

Installing a vanity unit in a bedroom or other room can be trickier because of the absence of suitable pipes to connect to.

The cold supply should ideally be drinkable, which means on a tank fed system you need to take a branch directly from the rising main. Often the easiest connection point is in the loft, where the main enters the cold storage tank.

The hot supply can be branched off any suitable hot supply pipe, or from the main supply pipe at the hot water cylinder. An alternative is to fit an individual under-unit electric water heater.

It's usually wise to select polybutylene plastic for both supply pipes, since this material is flexible enough to be threaded unobtrusively under floors, through hollow walls or along skirtings.

Drainage is likely to be the main problem unless the unit backs on to an outside wall near a stack; see Problem Solver below.

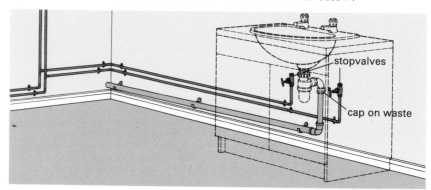

In the bathroom, run the supplies from suitable pipes and connect the waste to a hopper or internal plastic stack; fit stopvalves and temporarily plug the waste.

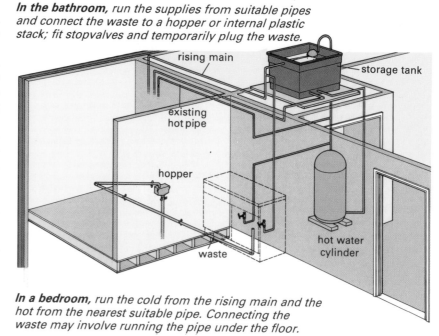

In a bedroom, run the cold from the rising main and the hot from the nearest suitable pipe. Connecting the waste may involve running the pipe under the floor.

◼ PROBLEM SOLVER ◼

Non-bathroom drainage
Where there's no connection point within close range, consider running the waste:
Under the floor If the joists run in the right direction (the opposite way to the boards), you may be able to run the waste straight out to a stack or hopper head.

Check by lifting a board and looking through with a torch and mirror; if there are bracing pieces nailed between the joists, the job's not on. Otherwise, simply make sure you use 40mm (1½″) pipe if the run is over 1.7m (6′ 6″) long.

Through the wall This is often overlooked, but if there's a bathroom on the other side the Building Control Officer may allow you to run a 32mm (1¼″) waste into a larger pipe via a *swept tee fitting.*

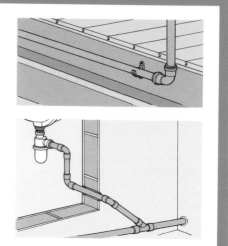

The waste (right) could run under the floor to an outside stack, or through the wall to another pipe.

PREPARING THE UNIT

Most units come flat-packed and need no more than a screwdriver to put together. But as with all self-assembly furniture you should read the instructions and identify all the parts before going ahead.

Leave the doors off until all the plumbing work has been completed, but fit the top – it's easier to cut *in situ*. You may have to notch or drill shelves to accept the pipes.

Cutting a basin hole

Many matched units are supplied with templates for cutting an inset basin hole. If not, or if you are adapting another piece of furniture, follow this sequence:

■ Pencil diagonal lines across the top from corner to corner, then measure along these lines by equal amounts and link the marks to form a square which you can use as a positioning guide. Draw in any obstructions below the top too, so you can avoid them when cutting.

■ Lay the basin upside down on the top and make sure it is positioned squarely – it may need to go nearer the back than the front if the edge of the top overhangs a front rail. If all is well, draw around the lip.

■ Measure the depth of the lip, then cut a piece of wood to the same thickness and use it like a scribing block (see Tip) to mark a cutting line inside the outer one. Rub out the first line to avoid confusion.

After marking, drill a hole inside the cutting line wide enough to insert a jigsaw blade, then cut through the top in the normal way. Support the top near the end of the cut to stop it breaking away – but not with your fingers.

Semi-countertop basins should be supplied with a template for the cut-out in the front of the unit.

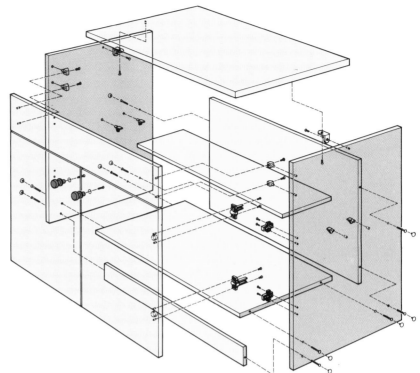

A typical self-assembly vanity unit. Work out beforehand where panels need to be drilled or notched for pipes or other obstructions. It may be easier to do this before you put the unit together.

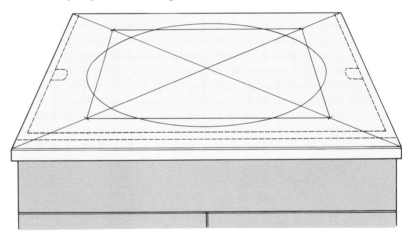

Marking out the top for an inset basin. Draw a square to provide a reference point for positioning and mark in any obstructions on the underside. In practice it may pay not to position the basin symmetrically.

Trade tip

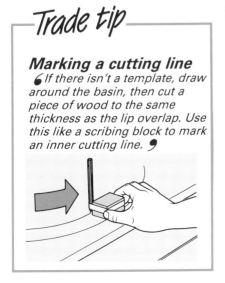

Marking a cutting line

❛If there isn't a template, draw around the basin, then cut a piece of wood to the same thickness as the lip overlap. Use this like a scribing block to mark an inner cutting line. ❜

Cut the hole for an inset basin using a jigsaw. Take care to support the waste as you near the end of the cut, and watch out for structural parts of the unit.

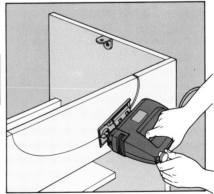

Fitting a semi-countertop basin may involve cutting out the front of the unit as well, though a template should be provided to match the basin profile.

MAKING UP THE BASIN

Make up the basin with taps and waste outlet in the normal way.

Taps are normally supplied with rubber and steel sealing washers, but on thin steel and acrylic basins you may need to replace those on the underside with *top hat washers* so that the nuts can get a grip.

Mixers may have 10mm flexible tails and compression joints already fitted. You can extend these via *flexible pipes* (and *reducing connectors* if there are no joints), but take care not to overtighten and strain the tails. Otherwise, fit *flexible tap connectors,* not forgetting the fibre washers used to make the seal at the tap tails.

Waste outlets for vanity basins come in several forms. *Pop-up wastes* (shown below) are part of the tap and must be dismantled for fitting. The lever arm on the pop-up connects via a ball and socket, and there may be a nylon cup washer to fit inside the capnut before it is tightened.

Conventional wastes for use with integral overflows are best bedded on plumber's putty – even where rubber washers are provided. Take care to align the slot in the outlet with the overflow channel.

Thin basins without overflows need *combined waste/overflows* similar to those found on baths. Bed *one-part wastes* in sealant, and apply a little more on the underside before and after threading on the overflow collar; then fit the washer and backnut and tighten. With *two-part wastes* secured by a screw through the grid, make sure the upper washer doesn't form a ridge around the grid; if it does, discard it and bed the grid in sealant.

Afterwards, fit the flexible overflow hose and threaded outlet.

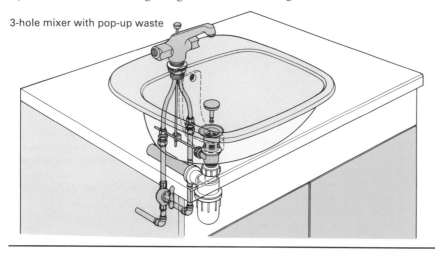

3-hole mixer with pop-up waste

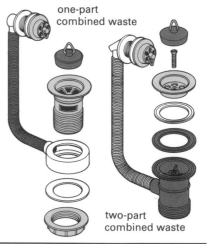

one-part combined waste

two-part combined waste

INSTALLING THE UNIT

For an inset basin, check the fit in the unit, then remove it and paint or varnish the edges of the cut-out to seal them. Follow by laying a bed of silicone sealant around the area covered by the lip – or fit the strip seal provided – then refit the basin and press down.

A china or resin basin may be held purely by sealant, in which case leave the basin weighted down overnight to ensure a good seal. Thin basins may have fixing clips on the underside: tighten these evenly, to avoid distortion.

Semi-countertop basins can be bedded on silicone sealant laid around the unit cut-out, but this isn't enough to hold them – most have additional wall or unit fixing brackets.

Installing the unit

Position the unit against the wall and check for level, then pack underneath if necessary using slips of plywood or old vinyl tile. The side panels may also need notching to fit over the skirting board or to accept the pipework.

When all is well, screw the unit to the wall and connect the plumbing.

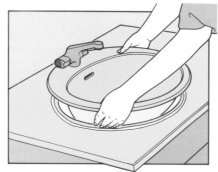

Bed an inset basin on silicone sealant, having first checked the fit. Thinner basins may have additional clips on the underside – tighten these evenly.

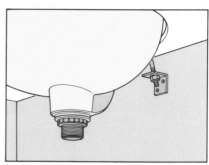

Semi-countertop basins can sit on sealant, but have additional wall or unit fixing brackets. Fit these once you have positioned the base unit.

Position and level the unit, then mark any wall fixing brackets. Remove the unit, drill and plug the holes, then re-level and screw to the wall.

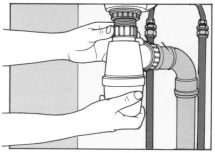

Make the final connections. Link the flexible tap tails or connectors to the supply pipes, then fit the bottle trap and connect up the waste.

CENTRAL HEATING REPAIRS – THE SYSTEM

Although water-filled ('wet') central heating systems vary widely in design, most work on the same basic principle and share the same basic problems. The majority of faults are easy to trace, and many can be put right without specialist knowledge or tools. But even if you don't fancy making your own repairs, knowing where the trouble lies can significantly reduce the cost of calling in a professional.

The chart lists common faults, together with possible causes and cures. Although it deals mainly with gas fired systems, apart from boiler faults the cures described apply equally to solid fuel and oil-fired systems.

The repairs in this section cover the **system** – pipes, boiler, radiators and so on. The following section deals with repairs to the electric **controls** – programmer, room thermostat and control valves – and all references to these are shown in italic type. In some cases, you may need to consult both sections in order to pinpoint the source of the trouble.

TROUBLESHOOTING GUIDE

SYMPTOM	CHECK (in order)...	POSSIBLE FAULT
Radiators cold, water cold	**Boiler** If pilot light is working... ...check programmer and room thermostat	Settings incorrect or controls faulty Electricity supply off
	Circulation system	Pump jammed/faulty
	If pilot light is not working... ...check gas is on ...check for draughts If it won't relight...	Gas supply cut off Pilot light blown out Faulty spark igniter Faulty thermocouple
	If it relights but goes out again...	Blocked gas jet (call engineer)
Radiators hot, water cold	Programmer and room thermostat Control valve Circulation system	Settings incorrect or controls faulty Valve jammed/faulty Airlock in pipes
Some radiators cold, water hot	Radiators	Airlock in radiator(s) Thermostat(s) jammed Valves need adjusting
	Circulation system	Water level too low Airlock in pipes Sludge in pipes
	Programmer and room thermostat	Settings incorrect or controls faulty
All radiators cold, water hot	Circulation valve Circulation system	Valve jammed/faulty Pump jammed/faulty Airlock in pipes Sludge in pipes
Heat on/off at wrong times	Programmer and room thermostat	Settings incorrect or controls faulty
Radiators too hot	Boiler	Thermostat incorrectly set or faulty
	Room thermostat	Thermostat incorrectly set or faulty
Water too hot	Boiler	Thermostat incorrectly set or faulty
	Cylinder thermostat (if fitted)	Thermostat incorrectly set or faulty
Hammering or kettling noise in pipes/boiler	Circulation system	Pipes scaled up Expansion noises Pump too fast/slow
Boiler lights with a 'boom' or goes out in strong winds	Boiler	Pilot light flame too weak or poorly adjusted or turbulence in flue (Call engineer)

For jobs in *italic type*, see pages 69-72.

ANATOMY OF A SYSTEM

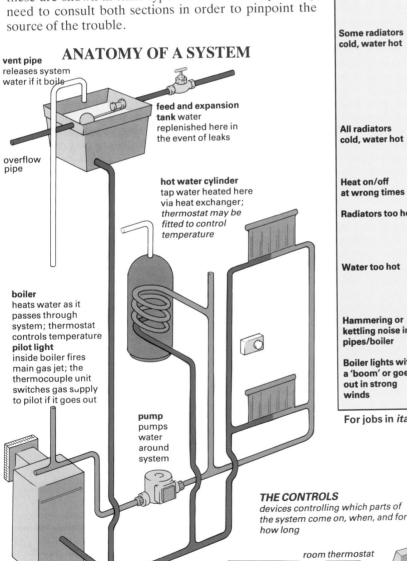

vent pipe releases system water if it boils

feed and expansion tank water replenished here in the event of leaks

overflow pipe

hot water cylinder tap water heated here via heat exchanger; *thermostat may be fitted to control temperature*

boiler heats water as it passes through system; thermostat controls temperature
pilot light inside boiler fires main gas jet; the thermocouple unit switches gas supply to pilot if it goes out

pump pumps water around system

drain cock

THE CONTROLS *devices controlling which parts of the system come on, when, and for how long*

room thermostat

programmer

control valve

Water heated by the boiler *flows around the system heating the radiators and hot water cylinder heat exchanger (which in turn heats hot water for the taps).*

In a ***fully pumped*** *system (left), all the water is pumped; control valves operated by the programmer determine whether it goes to the radiators, to the hot cylinder, or to both. In* ***gravity*** *systems, only the radiator water is pumped; hot water for the cylinder circulates continuously by convection (it rises to the cylinder as it is heated, and falls to the boiler as it cools).*

CURING BOILER PROBLEMS

Most people prefer to leave boiler repairs to an expert, but there are simple checks which you can make to pinpoint trouble spots.

If the pilot light is working, a sudden breakdown could be nothing worse than a blown fuse in the plug or FCU supplying the boiler. If the fuse is OK, check the electrical controls (see pages 69-72).

If the pilot light isn't working, switch off the supply and – if you haven't already done so – open the casing.

Pilot light problems

The pilot light unit is located at the foot of the boiler, directly in front of the burners. On most boilers there is an inspection hole to check the flame, but you may have to remove a screw-on cover to get a better view of the unit itself.

In most boilers the pilot burns permanently. When the programmer switches on the main gas supply to the burners, it is the pilot which lights them. But if the pilot goes out for any reason, a heat-sensing device called the *thermocouple* shuts off the gas supply to prevent leaks.

A pilot light which goes out may not relight for three reasons:

Faulty igniter Some boilers have a piezo-electric igniter, similar to those on gas hobs. On most models you can check if this has failed by holding down the igniter button and lighting the pilot by hand. If the pilot works, the igniter is faulty.

Faulty thermocouple When this fails, it shuts off the gas supply to the pilot light permanently. The cure is to have the thermocouple replaced.

Blocked gas jet If the pilot light only lights with difficulty, or splutters and burns feebly, the chances are the gas jet is blocked. Have the unit cleaned and adjusted.

Thermostat problems

Erratic temperature control of the system water (which in turn affects the heat of the radiators and tap water) points to a faulty boiler thermostat.

First, identify the thermostat dial, and the copper sensor tube which runs from the thermostat to a pocket in the heat exchanger.

■ Check setting on the dial. Unless otherwise specified, it should be at least 65 C (160 F) – or between 7-9 if the dial doesn't show temperature.

■ Check that the phial-shaped end of the heat sensor tube is securely located in the heat exchanger.

If all seems in order, the thermostat itself is probably faulty and must be replaced.

Getting help

The parts above are simple for an engineer to replace. Make things easier still by telling him what you think is wrong over the phone, and giving him the make and model number of the boiler.

To avoid future problems it's worth entering into an annual service contract. In the UK, check that the contractor is a member of CORGI (the Confederation Of Registered Gas Installers).

Other systems

The instructions given here apply to most types of gravity and fully pumped systems. However, they exclude:

■ *Pressurized* (unvented) systems, which are now allowed under the Building Regulations and found in some recently built homes.

■ *Combined* systems (eg Vaillant Combi) in which the boiler and hot water storage are combined in a single compact unit.

Both these systems require expert maintenance.

Turn off the power

Always turn off the power supply to the boiler and programmer (which automatically switches off the heating) before carrying out any repairs. If there is no separate plug and socket or fused connection unit (FCU), switch off at the fusebox.

Below: a typical gas boiler showing a close-up of the main gas valve, the pilot light unit, and the thermostat.

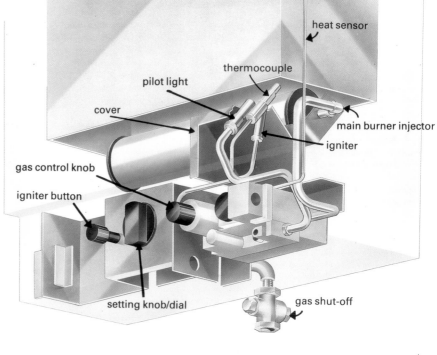

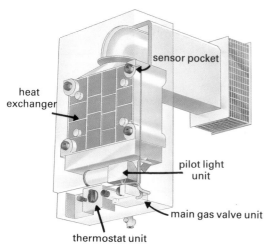

CIRCULATION PROBLEMS 1 – NOISE

Most noises in heating systems can be traced to one of two things:

Scale build-up on the insides of the pipes and the boiler heat exchanger is particularly common in hard water areas. The symptoms are howling, tapping or banging in the pipes, and roaring ('kettling') inside the boiler when it is firing.

Remove the scale by adding **descaling fluid** (available from builder's and plumber's merchants) and flushing out the system. Afterwards, add **corrosion inhibitor** to guard against future build-ups.

Expansion noise is caused by the pipes expanding and rubbing against their brackets or nearby objects as they heat up. It is most noticeable first thing in the morning. The cure is to track down all likely trouble spots and cushion them with foam so that the pipes can't rub against anything. Check, too, that the brackets are secure.

It's also possible that the pump – see overleaf – is running too fast or too slow. If yours has a speed setting dial, turn it up or down and see if this helps.

To add descaler or inhibitor, turn off the water supply at the expansion tank. Open the drain cock (see below) and draw off three bucketfuls of water...

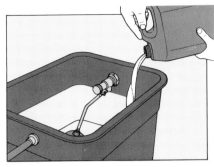

...then close again. Return to the expansion tank and pour in the relevant fluid following the maker's instructions. Afterwards, turn the water supply back on.

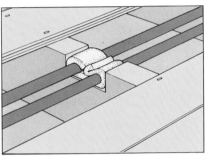

Use pieces of foam or insulation blanket to pack round pipes where they pass through joists or holes.

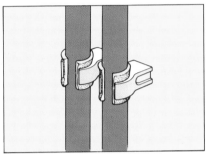

Pad pipe brackets with the same material if they look like they are a loose fit.

DRAINING AND FLUSHING THE SYSTEM

Draining the central heating water is done via the *system drain cock*. Normally there is only one – fitted on the boiler or one of the lowest radiators – but systems with complicated pipe runs may have more (in which case drain each in turn). Avoid airlocks by opening the radiator bleed valves (see overleaf), but give some of the water a chance to escape first.

Check the colour of the system water as it drains out: a deep black is normal; rust red points to severe corrosion – flush the system before refilling, and add a *corrosion inhibitor.*

Flushing and refilling

To flush, leave the drain cock open and restore the water supply at the expansion tank. Let the water run through the system for at least 30 minutes, then turn off at the tank again.

To refill, close the drain cock and open the tank stopvalve part-way so that the water enters slowly. Then, starting on the ground floor, close the radiator bleed valves one by one as the system starts to fill.

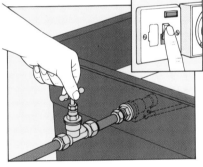

1 *Switch off the power, then turn off the water supply to the expansion tank. If there is no stopvalve, tie up the tank's ballvalve.*

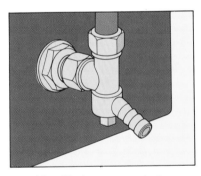

2 *Identify the system drain cock, which has a square shaped head and a small spout. Look for it near the boiler, or on the lowest pipe in the system.*

3 *Connect one end of a hose to the spout and run the other end to a nearby drain. Turn the drain cock head anticlockwise with an adjustable spanner.*

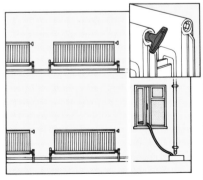

4 *Starting at the top of the system, open the radiator bleed valves one by one to release any air trapped during the draining process.*

CIRCULATION PROBLEMS 2 – PUMP & PIPES

The water level in the expansion tank is the first thing to check in the event of a circulation problem. The minimum depth is 100mm (4″) – any less, and the system won't function to full efficiency.

The drop in level is likely to be due to a stuck ballvalve, in which case wiggle the valve arm to free it.

Pump faults

The pump is a metal cased object around 125-150mm (5-6″) in diameter, which is usually plumbed into the system near the boiler or hot water cylinder. Check the pump is working with the heating switched 'on', and there are no loose wires.

Pumps have a habit of seizing up, particularly if the heating has been off for some time, but many types can be restarted without having to be dismantled. Look for a restart mechanism in the centre of the pump. It may be a screw slot (possibly under a plastic cover), or a small plastic knob. Switch off the power before you begin.

If the pump won't restart, or it is noisy enough to be heard (indicating wear in the bearings), it must be dismantled and probably replaced.

Airlocks and blockages

Airlocks in pipes tend to affect radiators higher up the system (they are rare in the hot water cylinder pipes). Start at the pump, which has a bleed valve fitted on the side of the casing. Some systems have further bleed valves (*aircocks*) at strategic points in the pipework.

Sludge blockages produce similar symptoms, but tend to affect pipes lower down the system. Minor blockages can often be shifted by speeding up the pump (see right). If not, drain the system and flush.

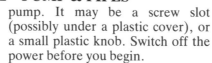
Trade tip

Shifting pipe airlocks

6 If your pump has a speed control, note the setting then turn it up to its highest point. Turn back after a few seconds and repeat at half-minute intervals.

If this doesn't work, run a hose from a mains-fed cold tap to the system drain cock and get a helper to check the expansion tank. Open the drain cock, then turn on the tap gently so that water flows into the system, pushing the system water (and any air) out via the expansion tank. Turn off the tap as soon as your helper sees the tank begin to overflow. 9

Note: Some water bye-laws require a *non-return valve* – available from plumber's merchants – to be fitted in the hose to prevent back-flow of the system water into the mains.

Check the pump is working with the controls set to 'heating on'. Rest a screwdriver against the casing, press to your ear and listen for a gentle whirring.

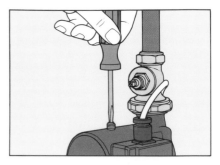

If the pump has jammed, rotate the screw slot with a screwdriver (or turn the knob) until you feel the rotor move freely. Water may dribble out, but this is normal.

Check for airlocks with the pump switched off. Unscrew the bleed valve a few turns and listen for the tell-tale hiss of air. Close the valve when water appears.

CURING RADIATOR PROBLEMS

Airlocks It is quite normal for small amounts of air to become trapped in the system and work their way round to the radiators, causing parts of them to go cool or cold.

Cure this by bleeding the radiators every so often using a special key. Fit the key in the valve, hold a cloth underneath, and turn anticlockwise. Close as water appears.

Thermostatic valves (TRVs) are fitted in place of conventional on/off valves to some radiators. They can jam in the closed position.

Unscrew and lift off the cover. Underneath is a pin, connected to the plastic diaphragm which opens and closes the valve. Move the pin up and down a few times with a pair of pliers to release the mechanism.

Lockshield valves are fitted on the opposite side to the on/off valves or TRVs to balance the flow of water through the system.

If one radiator refuses to warm up, unscrew the valve cover, then use an adjustable spanner to turn the head anticlockwise half a turn and see if this helps. Repeat if necessary, but only once.

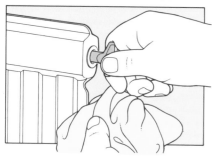

Bleed radiators using a special key. Turn anticlockwise and listen for the hiss of air.

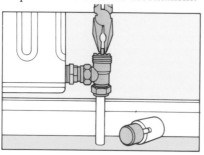

Thermostatic radiator valves can be freed by moving the diaphragm pin with pliers.

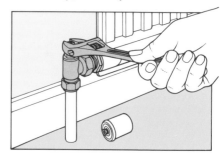

Adjust the lockshield valve if all else fails – but no more than one full turn.

CENTRAL HEATING REPAIRS – CONTROLS

Gas and oil-fired 'wet' (ie water-circulating) central heating systems rely on a series of electrical controls to turn the boiler on and off and monitor the output of heat or hot water. If one or more of these controls fails, or is incorrectly set, the system will run inefficiently – often reflected in higher fuel bills – and may break down altogether.

The Troubleshooting Guide on page 65 lists the symptoms associated with control failure and suggests which controls you should check. But not all systems are controlled in the same way, and some have more controls than others, so the first step towards tracking down faults is to examine your system and identify the key components.

Which system?

Some systems work on the *gravity flow* principle, in which the radiator part is pumped but the hot water part flows by convection (ie the water rises to the cylinder as it is heated and falls back to the boiler as it cools). In this case the controls are likely to be a simple combination of·programmer/boiler thermostat/room thermostat. How they work is described below.

If the system is *fully pumped*, in which all the water flows under pump pressure, a cylinder thermostat and control valves will be added to the list. The most common control set-ups for fully pumped systems are described overleaf.

Both types of system may also be equipped with thermostatic radiator valves, but these are mechanical devices which operate independently and don't affect the workings of the other controls.

THE KEY CONTROLS

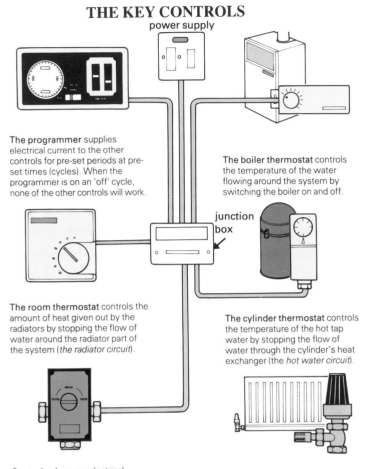

The programmer supplies electrical current to the other controls for pre-set periods at pre-set times (cycles). When the programmer is on an 'off' cycle, none of the other controls will work.

The room thermostat controls the amount of heat given out by the radiators by stopping the flow of water around the radiator part of the system (*the radiator circuit*).

Control valves are electrical devices enabling the thermostats to stop the flow of water through one circuit or another. They are usually plumbed into the system near the boiler or cylinder.

The boiler thermostat controls the temperature of the water flowing around the system by switching the boiler on and off.

The cylinder thermostat controls the temperature of the hot tap water by stopping the flow of water through the cylinder's heat exchanger (the *hot water circuit*).

Thermostatic radiator valves (TRVs) control the output of heat from individual radiators by shutting off the water flow.

CONTROLS IN A SIMPLE GRAVITY FLOW SYSTEM

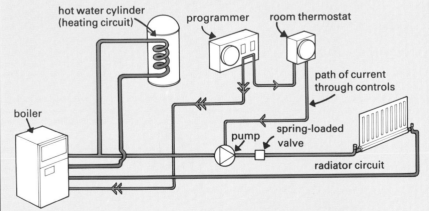
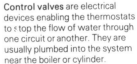

When the programmer is switched to an **'on'** cycle, current is passed to the boiler thermostat. This activates the boiler, which heats the system water.

If **'hot water only'** is selected, the current goes no further.

Water flows by convection around the hot water circuit, but is prevented from flowing to the radiators by a spring-loaded valve.

If **'hot water on, heating on'** is selected, the programmer passes on current to the room thermostat. This in turn passes the current to the pump, which overcomes the pressure of the spring valve and pumps water around the radiator circuit.

When the room thermostat senses that the house is hot enough, it shuts off the electrical supply to the pump. Water then reverts to flowing around the hot water circuit only. Meanwhile, the boiler thermostat will shut off the current to the boiler (which stops firing) as soon as the system water starts to exceed its set temperature.

When the programmer is switched to an **'off'** cycle, neither thermostat receives current and the system shuts down completely.

CONTROLS IN A PUMPED SYSTEM WITH ZONE VALVES

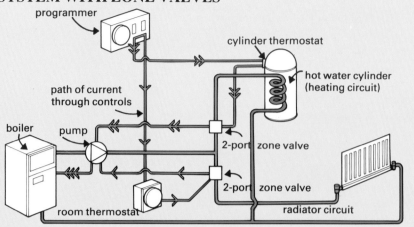

In all pumped systems, the path taken by the current after it leaves the programmer depends on which programme is selected.

When the programmer is set to **'hot water on, heating on'**, current passes to the cylinder thermostat and to the room thermostat. If either sense they are below their set temperatures, they 'call' for heat by passing on the current to one-way ('two-port') zone valves. The valves open, and switches inside them pass on the current again, this time to the boiler thermostat and pump. The system water is then heated and pumped around both circuits.

When one of the thermostats is 'satisfied' (ie reaches its set temperature), it shuts off the current to its zone valve, which springs closed and shuts off the current to the boiler and pump. Water then ceases to flow around this part of the system. If both thermostats are satisfied, no current passes to the boiler and

pump. The system then shuts down until a further call is made.

If **'hot water only'** is selected, only the cylinder thermostat receives current; the room thermostat remains inactive and its zone valve stays closed.

Likewise, some programmers have the facility to select **'heating only'**, in which case the room thermostat receives current and the cylinder thermostat remains

inactive during the programme.

At any of the above stages, the boiler thermostat will switch off the boiler if the system water starts to exceed its set temperature.

However, when the programmer switches to an **'off'** cycle, none of the thermostats receive current and the system shuts down regardless of whether they are 'calling' or 'satisfied'.

PUMPED SYSTEM WITH DIVERTER VALVE

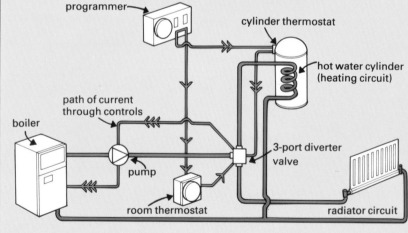

This arrangement works in the same way as the one above, except that the one-way zone valves controlling the hot water and radiator circuits are replaced by a single two-way ('three-port') diverter valve with outlets to both circuits.

Both the cylinder and room thermostats are connected to the diverter valve. When one of them 'calls' for heat, the motor inside the valve opens the outlet to that part of the system. Likewise, when the same thermostat is 'satisfied,' the outlet is closed off.

WHAT CAN YOU DO?

If the Troubleshooting Guide on page 65 leads you to suspect a control fault, first ensure that the controls are all correctly set – the single most common cause of central heating problems.

If all is well, carry out the tests described opposite on each of the controls in turn following the order:
Programmer
Room thermostat
Cylinder thermostat
Control valve(s)

(See pages 65-68 for checks on the boiler thermostat and TRVs.)

The tests are designed to help you track down the fault by a process of elimination. Professionals prefer the more reliable method of testing the current flowing through each wire in the control circuit using a circuit-tester screwdriver. However, this is not recommended for the amateur, due to the risk of confusing one wire with another while the power is on.

Safety first
The electrical current which powers central heating controls operates at mains voltage and is passed on to them via the programmer/boiler power supply (a 3 amp fused plug or FCU). Always check that this is off before opening up the controls or checking any wiring connections.

CHECKING THE PROGRAMMER

It's not possible to repair a programmer, so if it proves to be faulty it must be replaced. But first, make sure the connections between the programmer and its backing plate are sound.

- Turn off the power supply.
- Find the small screw holding the programmer to its backing plate (it may be hidden on the underside of the casing) and undo it.
- Lift off the programmer unit. Check that the wires running into the backing plate are all securely held in their terminals. Then check that the terminals linking the unit and backing plate are clean and making good contact.
- Replace the programmer unit, switch on the power and re-test.

Replacing a programmer

If you are sure the programmer is faulty, remove the unit again and take it to a plumber's merchant to obtain a matching replacement. This will simply slot on to the existing backing plate.

If you can't obtain an identical model, buy one offering the same functions and replace the backing plate as well. Check first that the terminals on both the existing and the new backing plate are labelled, so you know where the wires go.

To fit, remove the old backing plate from the wall leaving the wires intact, then fix on the new plate and transfer the wires one by one.

Water cold, radiators cold → Turn programmer to 'water on, heating on'; does boiler start after a few seconds?

→ **NO** → Try other programmes; does boiler start on any of them? → **NO** → Check connections to programmer; does this make any difference? → **NO** → Programmer faulty; replace

YES → Do heating/water come on? → **NO** → Check room 'stat, cylinder 'stat, control valve(s)

(from "Try other programmes" **YES**)

Water hot, radiators cold → Turn programmer to 'water on, heating on'; do radiators warm up? → **NO** → Check room 'stat, control valve

Water cold, radiators hot → Turn programmer to 'water on'; do radiators stay hot? → **NO** → Check cylinder 'stat and control valve

YES → Programmer faulty: replace

NB Some modern boilers are wired so that the pump stays on for a while after the programmer has shut the boiler down. This circulates the last remaining hot water round the system, saving it from going to waste.

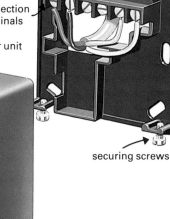

backing plate
plug-in terminals
connection terminals
securing screws

Most programmers plug into a separate backing plate which has terminals for the connections.

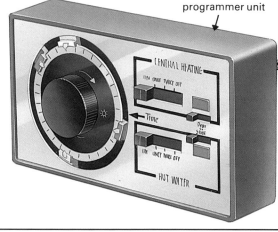

programmer unit

CHECKING THE ROOM THERMOSTAT

One of the first things to check on a room thermostat is that nothing in the immediate environment is triggering the heat sensor. Strong sunlight or a nearby fan heater will trip it prematurely, turning the radiators off, while draughts through a nearby door or window will cause the radiators to stay on long after they should have shut off.

Next, check the connections.

- Turn off the power supply to the programmer.
- Loosen the screw(s) holding the thermostat faceplate and lift it off.
- Check that the wires (there will be two or three) are held securely in their terminals.

If, after 'click' testing, the thermostat proves to be faulty, remove the wires one by one and note which terminals they run to. Then take the thermostat to a plumber's merchant and obtain a matching (or near-matching) replacement.

Radiators cold → Turn room 'stat up until click is heard; do radiators warm up? → **NO** → Check control valve (pumped system) or pump (gravity system); do they work? → **YES**

YES → Is room 'stat exposed to artificially high temps? → **YES** → Remove heat source

(from control valve) **YES** → Are connections to room 'stat sound → **YES** → Replace room 'stat

Radiators too hot → Turn room 'stat down until click is heard; do radiators go cold? → **NO** → Check control valve if fitted; does it work? → **YES**

YES → Is room 'stat exposed to draughts? → **YES** → Cure draughts or resite room 'stat

(from control valve) **YES** → Are connections to room 'stat sound? → **YES** → Replace room 'stat

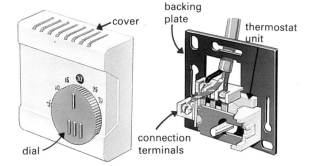

cover
backing plate
thermostat unit
dial
connection terminals

Room thermostats come in two parts – a faceplate and a backing plate. The electrical connections may be to either part, depending on the make and model.

CHECKING THE CYLINDER THERMOSTAT

Cylinder thermostats strap on to the side of the hot water cylinder. Before you do any tests, check that the strap is tight and that the back of the thermostat is in contact with the cylinder wall.

If the thermostat proves to be faulty, turn off the supply. Disconnect the wires one by one, noting their terminals, then unstrap the thermostat and take it to a plumber's merchant to obtain a matching replacement.

A typical cylinder thermostat (right) is in two parts and simply straps to the cylinder.

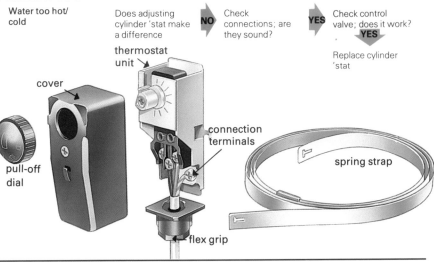

Water too hot/cold

Does adjusting cylinder 'stat make a difference **NO** Check connections; are they sound? **YES** Check control valve; does it work? **YES**

Replace cylinder 'stat

thermostat unit

cover

connection terminals

spring strap

pull-off dial

flex grip

CHECKING CONTROL VALVES

The control valve in question may have a coloured indicator or pointer to show it is working. If not, carry out the tests shown on the right.

Some makes of valve cannot be serviced, and if jammed or faulty must be replaced. This involves draining down the system and is covered in a later chapter.

However, on many newer models, it's possible to replace the entire motor unit (actuator) and free the valve spindle without interfering with the plumbing. Be sure to quote the make and model of the valve when ordering the replacement part.

With programmer set to relevant programme and room 'stat/cylinder 'stat on highest setting, do inlet and outlet pipes on valve warm up? **NO** Operate override lever (if fitted); do inlet and outlet pipes warm up now? **NO** Valve jammed

YES

Valve motor faulty (possibly the result of valve jamming)

Wiring in the new actuator flex is the trickiest part. The simplest way is to snip through the flex on the old actuator, then join it to the new flex via a **lighting BESA box** and block connectors (available from electrical and hardware stores).

■ Thread the old flex into the box and connect each wire to separate terminals on the block connectors.

■ Thread in the new flex and connect its wires to the same terminals, matching them colour for colour.

■ Screw on the BESA box cover and position the box so neither flex is under strain.

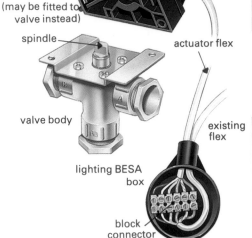

actuator

override lever (may be fitted to valve instead)

spindle

actuator flex

valve body

existing flex

lighting BESA box

block connector

A typical 2-way control valve, in which the actuator screws to a mounting plate. (On some models you need to remove the actuator cover to get at these screws.)

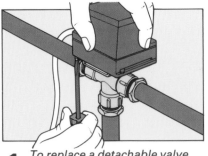

1 To replace a detachable valve actuator, first turn off the power. Then, depending on the make, pull off the actuator or unscrew it from the valve body.

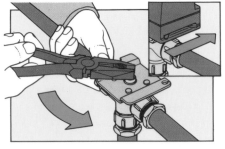

2 Check the valve isn't jammed by turning the spindle with pliers or moving the override lever. Even slight binding may have burnt out the actuator.

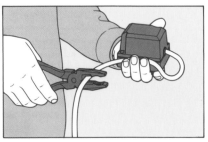

3 Cut through the flex at a convenient point and discard the old actuator. Prepare the end of the remaining flex as you would to wire an ordinary plug.

4 Connect the flex on the new actuator to the old flex via a BESA box. Fit the actuator to the valve, aligning the spindle with the slot in its base.

FITTING NEW RADIATOR VALVES

Fitting new radiator valves to replace ones which are old, jammed or leaking is a fairly straightforward plumbing job. However, you can use the same techniques to replace conventional valves with thermostatically controlled models (TRVs), so that the heat output of your central heating system is controlled on a room-by-room basis instead of relying on a single room thermostat.

Is it worth it?

Although TRVs can save on fuel bills by keeping individual rooms at a pre-set temperature, whether or not this justifies their cost depends on the rooms themselves and also on how the valves are used.

South-facing rooms which are warmed naturally by the sun, and spare bedrooms requiring only background heating, are two ideal locations. Most TRVs also include a frost setting for keeping the heating ticking over if the house is left empty during the winter.

On the other hand, living rooms which need a good level of heat all the time the central heating is running are unlikely to benefit much from TRV control unless there's a fire as well. And in any case you must leave at least one radiator open on a manual valve so that the pump doesn't meet undue resistance every time the heating switches on.

Whatever the room, the amount of fuel saved ultimately depends on people's willingness to keep the thermostats turned down – TRVs left on maximum setting all the time will save nothing.

.... Shopping List ....

Replacement valves and TRVs (see right) are widely available from DIY stores and plumbers merchants. They are generally sold complete with a new compression ring (olive), valve tail (see overleaf) and coupling nuts, so the only other material you need is PTFE tape for sealing the valve tail threads.

The only special tool required is a hexagonal Allen key for shifting the old valve tail – ask at your plumbers merchant. A hot air stripper may also come in handy to make releasing the joints easier.

TYPES OF RADIATOR VALVE

Manual valves fall into two categories: *handwheel* and *lockshield*. Handwheel valves are for turning the radiator on and off, and are usually (though not always) fitted on the flow side. Lockshield valves keep the flow through the radiator balanced and should be left undisturbed once set.

Most types work on the spindle principle, like stopcocks. However, a few more expensive models use expandable bellows instead of O ring seals, giving improved performance. Valves with built-in drain cocks are also available.

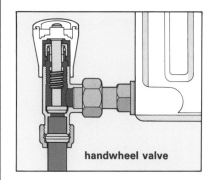 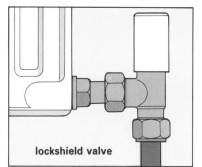

handwheel valve

lockshield valve

Thermostatic valves (TRVs) are fitted on the flow side of the radiator. A correctly set valve balances the flow automatically, so the lockshield valve on the other side of the radiator becomes redundant and can be left fully opened.

TRVs work by having a gas or liquid sealed in the *sensor head* which expands as the temperature rises, pushing a plunger on to a spring loaded spindle in the *body* to close the valve. There are numerous models to choose from, but look for the following features when buying:

■ Easily replaceable spindle O ring seals. These get a lot of wear, so it's helpful to be able to renew them without draining down the system. All types have replaceable sensors.

■ Remote sensors. These are an option on some valves, and give more accurate readings where the air flow around the valve is restricted by such things as furniture or long curtains.

■ Matching inlet and outlet fittings, allowing a choice of vertical or horizonal mounting on either side of the radiator. This could be important if space around the valves is restricted.

■ Ceramic disc operation. This costs more but helps to resist scale build-up, which can cause spindle valves to jam.

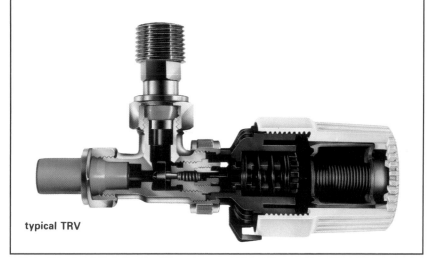

typical TRV

FITTING A NEW VALVE

Before fitting a TRV, start the system from cold and find out which pipe on the radiator gets hot first. The new valve must go on this side, irrespective of whether the current valve is a hand-wheel or lockshield.

It's a good idea to try the new valve in position so that you can check the fit. Make sure the flow direction stamped on the body matches the direction of flow through the radiator, and that the valve will fit in this position. Check, too, that you won't have to alter the pipe length to suit (see Problem Solver).

Draining the water

Before removing any valve, you should also decide how you're going to empty the radiator. The most reliable way, particularly if you're fitting several new valves, is to shut off the system and drain it down completely. However, there are alternatives:

■ If you have a pipe freezing kit, isolate the far side of the radiator by closing its valve, then freeze the pipe below the valve you want to remove. This still leaves the radiator full of water, which you must catch in a bowl as you unscrew the valve connections. It can be a messy job.

■ A Remrad kit allows you to force the water in the radiator back into the system pipes by attaching a bicycle pump to the air bleed valve at the top of the radiator.

Valve removal

■ Open the air bleed valve at the top of the radiator using a radiator key. (If you're draining as you remove the valve, open it gradually to start with.)

■ Place a bowl under the valve to catch any drips, then unscrew the valve/pipe connection with a wrench.

■ Unscrew the old valve from the threaded tail in the radiator.

■ Remove the threaded tail. The best tool for this is a hexagonal Allen key. Otherwise, try turning it with an adjustable wrench using a cloth to stop the jaws slipping. If it won't budge, warm the tail gently with a hot air stripper to soften the old jointing compound.

■ Remove the old olive on the flow pipe. Normally this can be done by tapping the nut upwards with a spanner. If not, saw through the olive carefully with a hacksaw blade.

Fitting the new valve

■ Remove the tail supplied with the new valve. Wrap four or five turns of PTFE tape around the thread, then screw the tail into the radiator.

■ Offer up the new valve (for a TRV, remove the sensor first), locate it against the tail, and check that the flow pipe meets the internal stop in the valve body. Then remove it and thread on the new nut and olive.

■ Refit the valve, tighten the pipe connection as for any compression fitting, then screw the valve coupling nut to the tail.

■ For a TRV, fit the sensor. Remote sensors screw to the wall and attach to the valve via a capillary tube.

RECOMMENDED TEMPERATURE SETTINGS

Living room 21°C	Kitchen 18°C
Bedroom 18°C	Hall 16°C
Bathroom 22°C	Study/playroom 21°C

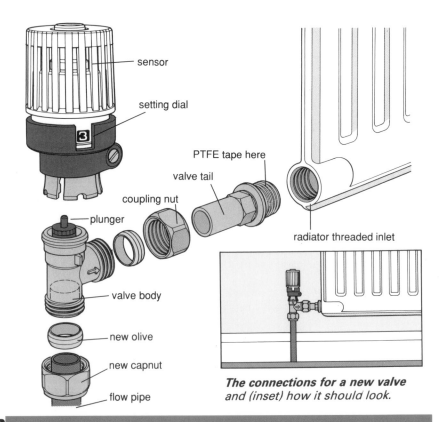

The connections for a new valve and (inset) how it should look.

PROBLEM SOLVER

Pipe too long/too short

To avoid leaks, it's essential that the flow pipe meets the internal stop inside the valve body; don't be tempted to 'make do' if it's just too short.

■ If the pipe is too long for the new valve, support it in an adjustable wrench (with cloth in the jaws) while you trim it to the right length with a hacksaw.

■ If it is too short, cut it back even further, then join in a new section. A soldered joint looks neatest here, but make sure the pipe is empty of water first, or the joint won't 'take'.

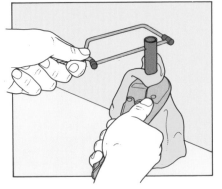

Support the pipe in a cloth-wrapped adjustable wrench if you need to trim off a small amount. Ensure the cut end is square, and file off any burr.

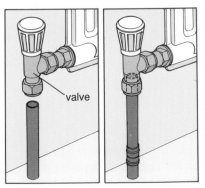

If the pipe won't reach the valve's internal stop, cut it back and join in a new section – preferably using a pre-soldered joint for neatness.

INSULATING PIPES AND TANKS

Insulating cold water supply pipes and storage tanks is a vital precaution against winter freeze-ups. But on hot pipes and the hot water cylinder, insulation can play another, equally important role – by keeping valuable heat sealed in and cutting down on fuel bills.

What to insulate

■ Top priority must go to pipes and tanks in the roof space, particularly if loft insulation has already been laid between the joists. This has the effect of lowering the temperature in the roof space, increasing its vulnerability to frost.

As well as the cold water storage tank and supply pipes, don't overlook the central heating feed and expansion tank, and the overflow pipes running from both tanks to the eaves. (Ice plugs here can easily cause ballvalve failures to pass unnoticed until it's too late.)

Next on the list are pipes passing through a cellar, garage, outhouse, utility room or non-centrally heated extension. These may survive cold snaps quite happily while the rest of the house is fully heated (ironically,

Trade tip

Is your house safe?

❛ Even if your pipes and tanks are already insulated, it pays not to be too complacent. Older insulation materials aren't particularly robust, and in time they have a habit of disintegrating or slipping off (especially in areas where repairs have been carried out).

It's also possible that whoever installed the insulation skimped on the job. Sadly, I've had plenty of customers over the years who thought they were safe from freeze-ups – but weren't. ❜

the escaping heat protects them). Yet it only takes one severe frost while the family is away to create complete havoc.

■ Check boxed-in pipes. If these run along cold walls, the boxing will insulate them from warmth in the house but not from cold outside.

■ Finally, check the hot water system. Hot pipes which pass through rooms can be left, as the heat they give out won't be wasted. But the hot water cylinder and any pipes inside cupboards are prime candidates for insulation – you can save around 75% of heat this way.

The instructions overleaf give suitable insulating materials for each location, so check before you buy. In some places you may be able to use up any materials left over from insulating the loft.

Insulate vulnerable pipework (below) using flexible foam sleeve insulation.

INSULATING PIPES

Protect pipes with *sleeve*, or *pipe-wrap* insulation. Each has its pros and cons, and it's often best to use a combination of both.

Using sleeve insulation

Insulating sleeve comes in two materials – plastic foam and felt.

Foam sleeve takes the form of rigid or semi-rigid tubes which come in various lengths, and in sizes to suit 15mm, 22mm and 28mm pipes. The tubes are slit lengthways – allowing them to be slipped over pipes – and either clip shut or are fixed with tape or wire depending on the make.

Foam sleeve is the most costly form of pipe insulation, but also the easiest to fit. To estimate, measure each pipe end to end (this covers wastage at joints) and total the figures. Round upwards to the nearest multiple of the sleeve length.

Make a note of any stopcocks, valves or other fittings. Some makes include special two-piece sleeve sections for these; otherwise, insulate them with pipe-wrap.

Felt sleeve is cheaper than foam and comes in rolls around 20m (22yd) long to suit 15mm and 22mm pipes. Although designed to be slipped over pipes before they are installed, it can be fitted to existing pipes by slicing open the stitched seams, then tying or taping in place.

Other materials: Suitable adhesive tape (see Tip), garden tie wire.

Tools checklist: Sharp knife, mitre box, tape measure, pliers.

rigid foam sleeve

traditional felt sleeve

home-made blanket roll bandage

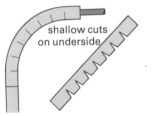

shallow cuts on underside

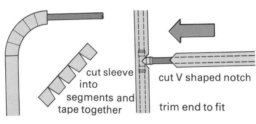

cut sleeve into segments and tape together

cut V shaped notch

trim end to fit

Trim foam sleeve as shown to deal with elbows, bends and T-junctions.

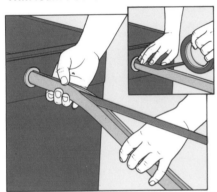

1 To fit foam sleeve insulation, prise the lengths apart and slip them over the pipe. On the non-moulded type, cover the split lengthways with tape.

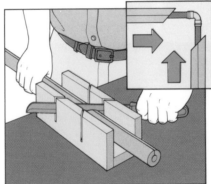

2 Tape lengths together where they butt-join. At corners, it's neater to mitre the ends in a mitre box – use a sharp kitchen knife to cut the sleeve.

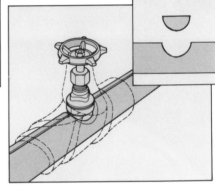

3 Cut notches in the sleeve to clear stopcocks and other fittings (see also Problem Solver). Where necessary, add an extra layer of pipe-wrap.

BOXED-IN PIPES

Insulate boxed-in pipes with **loose fill** loft insulation, which comes in bags of various sizes. Mineral wool loose fill is easier to handle than the granule type, but wear gloves – the fibres irritate the skin.

Open up the boxing at places which give good access to the entire pipe run, then push in the loose fill. Use an opened out wire coathanger for this part of the job, and channel the material through a home-made cardboard tube. Distribute it evenly over the pipes until they are completely covered.

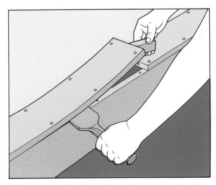

Unscrew the boxing at convenient points, or prise it open using a sharp bolster or old wood chisel. If necessary, prop the loosened end with a block of wood.

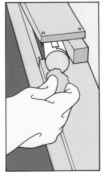

Force the loose fill into the boxing through a home-made tube of cardboard. Use a stick to push it through, then spread it evenly with an opened-out coathanger.

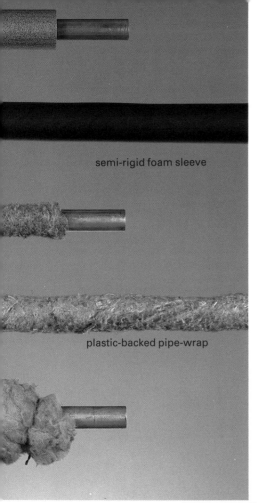

semi-rigid foam sleeve

plastic-backed pipe-wrap

Pipe insulation (left) comes in several different types.

Using pipe-wrap

Pipe-wrap (also called *bandage*) comes in rolls in a variety of materials, including felt, mineral wool and glass fibre. Some makes have a plastic or metal foil backing; others are self-adhesive, which makes fitting easier. Rolls are typically 50mm or 75mm (2–3") wide and 5m (16'5") or 10m (33') long. Make sure you compare like with like when checking prices.

Pipe-wrap is simply rolled around the pipes, overlapping on each turn. It is particularly useful on runs full of bends or joints, and for insulating stopcocks and valves.

Coverage is around half a metre of pipe per metre of roll, but treat this as a rough guide and err on the generous side – your supplier should be prepared to take back unused rolls if they're unopened.

Clean the pipes with a damp cloth before fitting self-adhesive pipe-wrap. For other types, cut lengths of wire to secure the ends.

Blanket roll left over from the loft can be used instead of pipe-wrap providing it is at least 50mm (2") thick. Cut the roll into 75mm (3") 'slices' using a panel saw. Then fix the home-made bandage in place with twists of wire or plastic tape.
Tools checklist: Trimming knife, panel saw (for blanket roll).
Other materials: Stiff wire or suitable adhesive tape (see Tip).

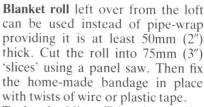

Tape tip

❝ At a pinch, you can use virtually any type of self-adhesive tape to secure foam sleeve, pipe-wrap and polystyrene slabs – but some types are better than others.

Some insulation manufacturers include purpose-made glass fibre reinforced or PVC tape as part of their ranges. A good alternative is 50mm (2") plastic parcel tape, sold by stationers. Don't use insulating tape, as it tends to lose its adhesion. ❞

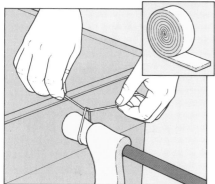

1 To fit pipe-wrap, start with a double turn and secure with a twist of garden tie-wire. Wind it around the pipe in a spiral, overlapping ⅓ of its width.

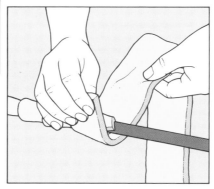

2 Allow a double overlap where lengths join. Secure the non-adhesive type with wire or tape – but not too tightly, or you'll reduce its effectiveness.

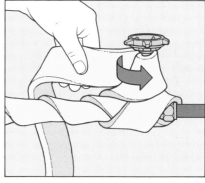

3 Wrap stopcocks and valves in an 'X' pattern so that the body of the fitting is completely covered, leaving only the handle exposed.

INSULATING THE HOT CYLINDER

Insulating jackets, consisting of quilted plastic sections filled with mineral or glass fibre wool, are available to fit all common sizes of cylinder. The sections are linked via a wire collar fitted around the topmost pipe, and held in place with elastic or adjustable straps. You'll find it easier to assemble the jacket if you fit the straps first.

If there is an immersion heater fitted, arrange for it to coincide with a joint between sections and leave the cap exposed. The same applies to a cylinder thermostat.

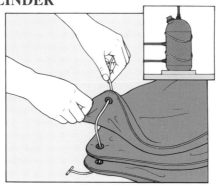

1 Fit the jacket's straps loosely around the cylinder, a quarter of the way from the top and bottom. Then thread the jacket sections through the wire collar.

2 Fit the collar around the top pipe and drape the sections over the cylinder. Tuck the sections under the straps, one by one closing any gaps as you go.

INSULATING TANKS

If you have the choice, insulate tanks **after** the pipework so that the vulnerable connections are doubly protected. Leave the area below a tank free of insulation to take advantage of rising heat.

Tank insulation kits consist of specially tailored slabs of polystyrene foam, plus tape or straps to secure them. They are made to fit all common sizes of plastic tank, but are unsuitable for round tanks and may not match older, galvanized steel types. Kits are not the cheapest solution, but they are easy to fit.

Slip-over insulating jackets similar to hot water cylinder jackets are available for round tanks.

For either of the above options, be sure to measure the tank dimensions before you buy.

Polystyrene slabs used for loft insulation are easily cut to fit square-sided tanks. The slabs should be at least 25mm (1″) thick. Fix with cocktail sticks and tape.

Left-over blanket roll or batts (minimum 75mm [3″] thick) can also be used, but they are less robust than slabs and trickier to fit. Secure the pieces with string, and tape over

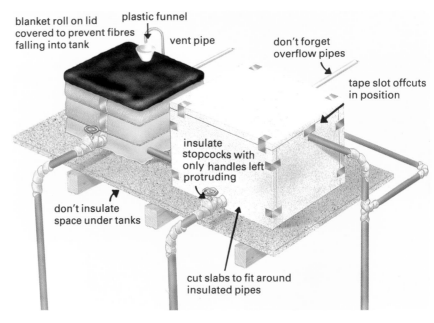

blanket roll on lid covered to prevent fibres falling into tank

plastic funnel

vent pipe

don't forget overflow pipes

tape slot offcuts in position

insulate stopcocks with only handles left protruding

don't insulate space under tanks

cut slabs to fit around insulated pipes

any vertical joints. Cut another piece to fit on top of the lid and wrap them both in a bin liner.

Where the tank is without a lid, make one from an offcut of 12mm (½″) chipboard or 9mm (⅜″) plywood. Cut slots to clear pipes, then drill out the waste wood.

Other materials: Suitable adhesive

A properly insulated cold storage tank/central heating expansion tank set-up showing polystyrene slab and blanket roll insulation.

tape (see previous page), string or twine, cocktail sticks, funnel.

Tools checklist: Sharp kitchen knife, tape measure, felt-tip pen.

1 **Cut foam slabs** to fit around the sides of the tank using a sharp kitchen knife. Cut slots to clear any pipes, but save the offcuts for taping back on.

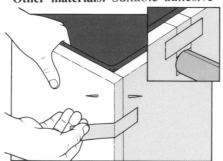

2 Fix the slabs together at the corners with cocktail sticks and reinforce with PVC tape. Then tape back the offcuts where slots were cut for pipes.

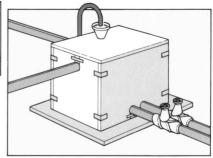

3 Cut a fifth slab for the lid and secure to the sides with tape. Where there is an overhead vent pipe, drive a cheap plastic funnel through the slab.

PROBLEM SOLVER

Awkward areas

There are likely to be places where space is too restricted to fit conventional insulation. In particular, watch out for outside taps and the holes where their supply pipes pass through walls. There may be a similar problem at the eaves, where overflows pass to the outside.

Pack these gaps with expanding foam filler, available in aerosol form. Although not cheap, it provides better weather protection than loose fill and is easier to handle.

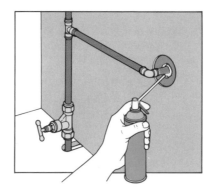

Squirt foam filler into the gaps where supply or overflow pipes pass through outside walls.

Cover outside tap pipes in a 'sleeve' of foam. This can be sanded smooth when dry.

INDEX

ACKNOWLEDGEMENTS

Photographers
AEG 53(t); Armitage Shanks 59; Armstrong 75; Barking Grohe 41, 45(t), 45(b); Caradon Mira 55; Eaglemoss (Peter Barry) 49(t), (Jon Bouchier) 9, 12, 13, (Derek St Romaine) front cover(tr), 25-27, 29, (Steve Tanner) 17, 49(b), 53(b), 76-77; Franke front cover(tl); Graham Builders Merchants 6; Robert Harding Picture Library 1(tr), 4; Hurlstons 1(tl); The Kitchen Consultancy 2; Myson 73; Pegler 45(c); Svedberg 61; Texas 60; Thos. Dudley 33-34; Elizabeth Whiting Associates (Neil Lorimer) front cover(br).

Illustrators
Neil Bulpitt 7-8, 65-68, 75-78; Jeremy Dawkins 7-8; Paul Emra 10-12, 13-16; Mark Franklin 49-52; Jeremy Gower 10-12, 13-16; Andrew Green front cover(bl), 17-20, 21-24, 25-28, 29-32, 37-40, 41-44, 45-48, 49-52, 54, 55-58, 59-64, 65-68, 69-72, 73-74, 75-78; Alex Jessel 41-44; Maltings Partnership 33-36; Stan North 29-32, 54, 69-72.